THE STRESS BOOK

Forty-Plus Ways to Manage Stress & Enjoy Your Life

THE STRESS BOOK

Forty-Plus Ways to Manage Stress & Enjoy Your Life

D. Terrence Foster, MD, FAAPMR, DABPM

Global Health and Consortium Publishing

GHC[P]

Publisher: Global Health and Consortium. GHC[P]

PO Box 824, Morrow, GA 30260.

Printed in the United States of America. No claim to Original United States Government Work.

First published in September 2021.

Library of Congress Cataloging in Publication Data

The Stress Book, Forty-Plus Ways to Manage Stress & Enjoy Your Life: D Terrence Foster. M.D
ISBN: 978-1-7375192-2-5 (Paperback).

Library of Congress Control Number: 2021942486

Also available
1SBN: 978-1-7375192-0-1 (Kindle)
1SBN: 978-1-7375192-3-2 (Hardback)
1SBN: 978-1-7375192-1-8 (eBook)

DISCLAIMER

This publication is intended to inform and educate the general public and medical providers. Therefore, the subject matter encompasses many areas related to stress. Also, the subject matter continues to change and evolve. Because of these reasons and others, readers are advised to consult with their personnel for medical, legal, or financial advice.

This book is intended for national and international publication. The laws of each country are different; hence the information provided may not necessarily reflect the readers' state or country. The author has taken great care in researching and presenting the facts in this book. Every effort has been made to ensure that this book is free of error. Regardless, the author and publisher do not assume any responsibilities or liabilities for errors or omissions. Also, all liabilities are disclaimed from using any or part of the information from this book.

For the suggested readings, references, and resources listed, every effort has been made to obtain and give credit for all the material we have used that required copyright release. If for any reason any content appears in this book that does not have the author's or publisher's permission, we apologize for the error of omission.

DEDICATION

To everyone who has lost someone or suffered in the coronavirus (COVID -19) pandemic.

TABLE OF CONTENTS

INTRODUCTION

What This Book Is About

If I were to ask, are you stressed or feeling stressed, what would your answer be? There are so many things out in the world today that are impacting our lives. Therefore, we are feeling stressed. Almost all of us are experiencing some level of stress, now more so than ever

In this book, I will be discussing some of the best ways of reducing and preventing the elevation of our stress levels. I will be looking at how we can effectively deal with stress, the various factors that cause stress, and some strategies that can effectively reduce or prevent stress in our lives. The level of stress, the various factors contributing to its elevation, and how we best manage these factors are thoroughly discussed in this book.

The information presented in this book allows it to be used in some instances as a teaching guide, scholarly reference, or a source for therapeutic stress management. In addition, the concepts and theories presented can create a framework in which research can be conducted to validate them further.

Also presented in this book is a description of a potential new mental disorder associated with the termination of relationships, particularly toxic ones. This disorder I called Abstract Kidnapping Disorder – AKD. It is covered in Chapter 14.

By the end of this book, you should understand not only how to manage stress but how to take control of the things that are adversely affecting you and how to create a structure and foundation that will enable you to enjoy your life.

About Me and Why I Wrote This Book

The idea to write this book came about during the heights of the coronavirus pandemic in the year 2020. I did a YouTube video about stress and found that even though the information I provided was limited, the video and its content were well received and beneficial to many. One of my primary goals in life is to help others. The writing of this book is consistent with attaining that reality.

Let me share some of my personal experiences. The need for this book is, without a doubt, clearly significant. We all experience stress. However, the nature of stress is complex. Understanding it requires not just experiencing stress but also having a more in-depth insight into stress and its impact on each person and society as a whole. I have been practicing medicine for more than twenty-five years. A significant part of my practice involves treating chronic pain patients with an associated high level of stress, often some psychiatric disorders, and other comorbidities, all of which can exacerbate stress levels in those patients and myself.

With respect to my professional and personal life, I am the chief medical officer of a licensed pain clinic. My role in part is to evaluate and treat patients in chronic and acute pain. Some of these patients often include those who have failed to respond to treatment from other medical providers. Treatments include opioids, other controlled substances, and other management options. As a consultant and continuing treating physician, my role is to provide management protocol often for "these difficult patients" in a pain management setting/clinic.

Another aspect of my practice that involves stress is managing a clinic that is certified to treat patients who are suffering from addictions to opioids with Suboxone. This is one of several prescription medications used to treat some of those individuals addicted to opioids, legal or illegal. In general, many of these patients who require Suboxone are often some of the most challenging patients to manage medically. This is partly because of a range of medical, social, and psychological issues that are often very complex to address in just about anyone who is addicted to a substance. In addition, most of these patients are often unable to afford the costs of the medical care that they do need. However, they often do not have any healthcare coverage. Also, the regulatory and administrative management add more stress in taking care of them.

I am a pain management or a pain medicine doctor and board-certified. In addition to managing patients with medications, a significant part of my practice is Interventional Pain Management, which involves in part spinal interventional procedures. Now, even though, with time and experience, these procedures become more routine and manageable, there are always inherent risks involved, and hence an associated level of stress for each procedure that is performed. Furthermore, these procedures in the wrong hands can lead to significant complications or even deaths.

I'm also the medical director for a personal injury clinic. This involves frequent interactions with many different attorneys and dealing with litigations, depositions, interviews, and various communication levels as a routine part of this practice. This, at times, can be very adversarial and, without a doubt, often adds a significant level of stress that is built into every personal injury medical practice.

The moment a personal injury patient walks into our office, if we decide to accept and treat that patient, we are also committing ourselves to be fully involved in any and all litigations and associated legal proceedings concerning that patient. Involvement includes the attorney representing them, the attorney of the opposing side, and possibly others.

I previously served as the medical director of an acute inpatient rehabilitation center for ten years. While at the same time, involving in some of these things that are listed.

In general, healthcare and the practice of medicine are never-ending, complex professions with new regulations and protocols that, in general, make it challenging to manage any successful medical practice. This is often very difficult and stressful, and being the chief operating officer of one such practice is indeed additionally stressful.

I also have other professional responsibilities: I serve on the board of directors of three non-profit organizations. I am also the CEO/Chairman of the D. Terrence Foster Foundation Inc., a non-profit organization, as well as involved in other charitable and civic organizations.

I do have other business ventures that also add to my responsibilities and stress level.

I am a Youtuber with a channel (Dr. D. Terrence Foster) that is growing and requires time, effort, and a significant level of responsibility.

With all of these professional responsibilities, I must continue maintaining the required credentials and board certifications as a medical doctor. These often require continued medical education, courses, examinations, conferences, and lectures, among other responsibilities.

In addition to all the above, there is all the everyday stuff—maintaining a home, paying bills, communicating, dealing with, and managing people, relationships, and events daily.

Finally, I am a parent with a personal family and an extended family. I love them all but let's just say we are a work in progress, definitely not without stress. And here I go again, writing another book.

I mentioned some of the potentially stressful aspects of my life as someone who is writing about stress to give you a personal view or an insight into my world. Each of us will have our own stories of our "baggage" and our daily challenges as we travel on this journey called life.

Our stories may be different, and our paths may also be different, but one thing for sure is we will all experience stress. My task will be to give you some insight into the strategies and solutions that are very important in managing stress with the hope that they will be helpful in your life. And though our experiences may be different or similar in some ways, my life experiences professionally and personally allow me to speak on this topic we call stress.

The Layout of This Book

This book is divided into four sections and twenty-two chapters. Section One explains the basics of stress; Section Two covers physical actions; Section Three covers mental actions; and Section Four covers community actions required in stress management and prevention. In this book, I will introduce a concept in the management and treatment of stress called **Foster's Stress Action Plan**, which utilizes two acronyms, **P.A.M.A.C.A** and **S.T.R.E.S.S.** (discussed in Chapters 1c & 2). Also included in this book are forty-plus actions that can be taken to reduce or prevent stress. This stress action plan will change the way we manage stress and significantly improve stress reduction when applied. Most of the chapters will end with several important points referred to as "Words of Caution or Comments." These points are intended to help provide an increased level of clarity and emphasize essential concepts or ideas.

How to Use This Book: The first section (one), The Basics of Stress and its Management, will provide you with some basic information about stress. It is essential that everyone reads chapter 1a before moving on to the next. Chapters 1b and 1c may appear challenging to some, but most readers will fully understand the presented information. For the remainder of the book, the chapters can be read sequentially, or in any order you choose or prefer. You will still have a good understanding of stress management, the many factors contributing to stress, and how best to deal with them. Now, even though you may be reading out of the chapter's sequence from each section, it will still be evident to you what are the related actions of stress, whether it be physical, mental, or community actions that are relevant to stress management.

Why Should You Read This Book and How Will You Benefit from Doing So?

I hope that the new concepts and ideas that are contained in this book will provide at least in part a better understanding and a framework that encompasses some of the tools and strategies that are essential for effective stress management. If these are implemented, they will allow each person who reads this book the opportunity to be equipped with helpful and practical solutions that are extremely useful in managing stress. Of course, because we are all so different, there is not one particular approach that will work for everyone. However, I hope that each of you will find something beneficial from reading this book. I also hope that when you have completed reading this book, or even before you finish it, at least one of the following states will be yours—at ease, happy, relaxed, calm, assured, unbound, restful, serene, uninhibited, cheerful, confident, tranquil, loose, unflustered, unshakable, content, unworried, at peace, easygoing, even-tempered, laid-back, and self-assured—as you strive to conquer stress.

The reality is there are so many things and circumstances that create stress or are stress factors in our lives that warrant understanding and knowledge. This book highlights them.

More than a stress book: Now, although this book is about stress, there is so much information in this book that will teach and help you live a more productive and successful life. This book also has the potential to transform your life if you are willing to open your mind and embrace new possibilities along the path of life's journey. This can be accomplished by simply utilizing some of the information and implementing some of the actions presented in this book.

What This Book Is Not or Will Not Do

This book will not provide details of the pathophysiology, the anatomy, or theories behind stress and its manifestation. However, as a scientist and a medical doctor, I believe it's my obligation to let you know that stress does have a scientific basis. And in general, the presence of stress or its effects on the human body can be explained scientifically. Therefore, in this book, I have only included a basic description of stress with respect to the anatomy and pathophysiology involved (see Chapter 1b).

The next thing that I need to point out is: I have asked many questions or raised many issues in this book. The main objective of that is to stimulate you into action to help find solutions for stress and, in some cases, provide you with the framework and resolution for improvement of the level of stress you are experiencing. It is definitely not practical or even possible to give details of every issue or question that I have raised or highlighted. So, the onus is on you to expand your knowledge about these fundamental issues that contribute to stress and make your lives that much more difficult as you face increasingly stressful and challenging situations.

Quotations: There are so many great thought leaders that have helped shape our minds and often the actions we take in our lives. Some of them have made their transition, and others are still here with us. I have included some quotations in this book, primarily because I believe in part that they echo or express similarities to some of the concepts, ideas, or information presented in this book. Some of them are attributed to multiple sources or authors; therefore, the names listed are the ones most commonly associated with them.

It is also important for you to know that including these quotations in this book does not endorse everything these persons represent, support, or stand for. Neither is the presence of their quotations represents or implies an endorsement or support of any kind from them or their representatives for this book or any part of it unless otherwise specified. Personally, I believe that there is good and evil in everyone. We often hope that the better part of each person's humanity will prevail as we go through this journey called life.

Finally, it is my intention that this book will make a difference in some people's lives or in the lives of those we hold close to and are most dear to us.

SECTION ONE

THE BASICS OF STRESS AND ITS MANAGEMENT

CHAPTER 1A

What is Stress, and Why Are You Stressed?

So, what is stress? Stress in the context of the practice of medicine is a physical, mental, or emotional condition that causes bodily or mental tension or emotional strain. It may also be a factor that causes diseases or can be a contributing factor to numerous diseases. One can have acute stress, episodic acute stress, or chronic stress. Each type of stress will have its duration or lifespan, which will determine how long the stress lasts and how we treat or manage it when a person is experiencing being stressed.

You see, stress can manifest in so many different ways. For example: how do we deal with palpitation symptoms, difficulty breathing, tightness in our chests, or many different feelings or emotions? Often these symptoms make our lives so much more challenging to live and, more importantly, thrive and enjoy.

In medical science, **Dr. Hans Selye** was a Hungarian-Canadian endocrinologist[3,4,5] who is credited as being the first to demonstrate the existence of biological stress. Thus, he is considered the "father of stress research."

Sometimes stress is categorized into three main types: **calm, eustress, and distress**. Calm is the state of little or no stress. The performance level associated with stress is highest during eustress and lowest in a state of calmness or distress. In contrast, distress is a stress level beyond the normal level to severe, a state that negatively impacts the person experiencing that stress level significantly.

Eustress, according to the *Merriam-Webster Dictionary*, is a form of stress having beneficial effects on health, motivation, performance, and emotional well-being. In general, a moderate or normal amount of psychological stress is considered beneficial to those experiencing stress. Hence stress is not all bad or always negative; it may have a positive outcome.

For example, you may get a new promotion. You may have bought a new home or a car. How about a new addition to the family, a newborn? All these are very positive things, and they often come with responsibilities. From that perspective, as fulfilling and rewarding or accomplishing as each may be, any or all of these can and will add stress to varying degrees. ***The question is, how do we deal with all this stress?***

Some other types of stress are associated with relatively ordinary things. These include: going to school or college, working, having a job, which is extremely important but comes with added stress. Also, driving to work, living in a relationship that you hate, or feeling trapped, but you somehow accept that as your normal life.

Stress may be brought on suddenly. For example, you could lose your job, be going through a divorce, be involved in an accident, or be robbed or assaulted, which can have severe or even involve deadly consequences. Some of these stresses in and of themselves are traumatic, physically, and/or emotionally.

Bear in mind that our environment or our body and mind also can become stressors. This means whatever thought is going through our minds can determine the level of stress we have at any given time. Whatever illness, condition, or state our body is in also can lead to stress. What are we experiencing? Are we experiencing a pandemic, lots of violence in our community, fighting, or something else? These things can also lead to stress.

Some stress may be short-term. Some may be long-term, and other cases may be ongoing. But stress in any event, in general, is considered a normal occurrence or normal way of life for all of us, depending on the level we are experiencing and its impact on us. But yes, we all have stress. Now, your stress may be different from mine. For example, I may have a stress level that I consider to be normal, and for others, it may be too much, or somebody may have a lot of stress that for me maybe too much and for them is just normal.

So how do we know that we are experiencing stress? The first thing is that we must pay attention so that we can and will recognize the various signs and symptoms that our body is showing us or revealing to us. Chronic stress over time will contribute to many serious health problems, with multiple signs and symptoms. Some of them will be obvious, and some will not. Some of the signs and symptoms will indicate the presence of disease or at least the possibility of illness. **These may include emotional symptoms—moodiness, irritability—and psychiatric or psychologically related symptoms—such as agitation, anxiety, depression, or a general sense of wanting to be alone**. An individual may feel overwhelmed or easily angered, becoming very angry without much provocation or with minor irritation. Someone could be at a level where they are so stressed that it really does not take much for them to feel out of control and respond outside the norm of what is considered the typical, expected reaction.

In addition to these signs and symptoms there are others, such as cardiopulmonary, cardiac, and related medical problems. For example, you may experience palpitations, tachycardia (where someone may feel their heart pumping or beating out of their chest), or you may have shortness of breath.

The *Diagnostic and Statistical Manual of Mental Disorders, 5th Edition* (DSM-5) includes acute stress disorder (ASD) in the category "Traumatic and Stress-Related Disorders." Also in this category is adjustment disorder (AD) and post-traumatic stress disorder (PTSD). Stressful or traumatic events generally cause disorders in this category. An individual involved in traumatic events may develop ASD; this is also called psychological shock, mental shock, acute stress reaction, or traumatic stress disorder.

There is a myriad of conditions that are not just limited to one body part or one organ system of the body (see the following table).

SOME CONDITIONS ASSOCIATED WITH STRESS	
EMOTIONAL RELATED SYMPTOMS	OTHER SYMPTOMS
Anxiety and Agitation	Cardiac (Heart Disease)
Unhappiness	Palpitation - Tachycardia
Loneliness and Isolation	Hypertension - High Blood Pressure
Moodiness, Irritability,	Shortness of Breath
Feeling Overwhelmed	Diabetes
Problem Sleeping	Headaches
Biting of the Nails	Dizziness or Lightheadedness
Fidgeting and Pacing	Muscle Tension: Neck, Face, or Shoulders
Grinding Teeth, Clenched Jaw	G.I. SYMPTOMS
Cold and Sweaty Palms	Weight Gain, Weight Loss
Trembling and Shaking	Upset Stomach, Diarrhea
Sexual Difficulties/Disorders	Indigestion or Acid Reflux Symptoms
Tiredness, Exhaustion	Irritable Bowel Syndrome
Anger	Change in Appetite

The symptoms of traumatic and stress-related disorders range from irritability to anger, sleep disturbance, and difficulty concentrating. Some symptoms are similar to those seen with anxiety: chest pain, palpitations, and gastrointestinal issues. Individuals who have sustained acute traumatic events that persist for more than one month may be referred to as having a PTSD diagnosis. Some symptoms may affect multiple organ systems, particularly when stress becomes chronic.

Still, the entire body can become involved in the manifestation of stress or stress-related signs and symptoms. Therefore, being aware of stress, the associated signs, and symptoms and understanding how one may respond to stress or its manifestations are vital factors essential in managing and treating stress. Knowing that when one is experiencing stress to the point when it is adversely affecting them, the question is, what do we do? That is, in part, what this book will hopefully allow you to see and get a better sense of how we can manage stress in our lives.

From their 2014 stress statistic, the American Institute of Stress listed the top five causes of stress in the United States: job pressure, money (these two account for 76 percent of the cited cases), health, relationships, and poor nutrition.[10,11] They also stated that 77 percent of U.S. individuals experience physical symptoms caused by stress, while 73 percent of them had psychological symptoms caused by stress.

The Global Organization for Stress[9] compiles other relevant data and statistics regarding stress. This organization lists its mission statement as: "To bring you stress solutions, stress management strategies, stress relief techniques, and stress research from around the globe."

Stress continues to be a global issue affecting just about everyone. Since the coronavirus pandemic of 2020, statistics have shown that stress level has significantly increased over the previous twelve months in 2019 before the pandemic. Seventy-five percent of adults reported a moderate to high level of stress during the pandemic. The problem is compounded by the underlying stress that existed before the pandemic.

CHAPTER 1B

The Anatomy of Stress

I believe this book would be incomplete without at least giving a brief introductory overview of the scientific basis of stress. You could read about the hypothalamus, pituitary-adrenal axis, the autonomic nervous system, the main areas in the brain responsible for stress, and its modification. The limbic system, hippocampus, amygdala, cerebral cortex, prefrontal cortex, and other structures also play essential roles in the process. You will understand that the brain's and the nervous system's coordination and interaction with these structures and others are crucial. They modify stress by producing and/or releasing endogenous substances included but not limited to hormones. These include adrenaline/epinephrine, norepinephrine, cortisol, melatonin, and the body's natural endorphins, oxytocin, dopamine, and serotonin. The involvement of the vagus nerve in the autonomic nervous system is also part of the process.

The scientific basis of stress, although complex, is well documented. As in so many other organ systems, the brain plays vital roles and is the main controlling organ regulating stress processes. There are many specific structures of the brain, and hormones that are important concerning stress and its regulation.[26] The following is a list of some of them and a brief description of their functions: There is also significant research ongoing in this area of science concerning stress.

The limbic system is a group of brain structures that work together to regulate the body's physiologic and psychological functions. These include but are not limited to emotional and behavioral regulations, both consciously and unconsciously. For example, these are associated with flight or fight response, response to fear or stress, feeding, taking care of oneself, motivation, learning, and a myriad of others.

It is believed that the **limbic system** structures are the **amygdala, hippocampus**, and cingulate gyrus. In addition to these, there are other brain structures. These include the **prefrontal cortex**, part of the thalamus, the fornix, the basal ganglia, and possibly others.

The cerebral cortex is responsible for many functions that play a role in stress directly or indirectly.

Specifically, the **prefrontal cortex** is the brain area that is primarily responsible for executive or cognitive function. This includes planning, decision-making, self-control, and problem-solving, among other functions. This brain area receives sensory inputs or information that it interprets and communicates to other areas of the brain to create the desired functional response, without which rational and successful strategies and achievements in life are impossible. Without this part of the brain working correctly, a variation of the desired outcome will result.

The hypothalamus controls the body's hemostasis (maintaining the balance of metabolism/various reactions or physiology) by producing and or causing the release of hormones and controlling the autonomic nervous system's function.

The hypothalamus-pituitary-adrenal axis (HPA - Axis) comprises three main structures responsible for stress modulation. These structures are the hypothalamus, pituitary gland, and adrenal glands.

They consist of many endocrine-secreting glands, each secreting its own hormones. The hypothalamus controls the release of many hormones from the pituitary gland.

One of them is the **corticotropin-releasing hormone (CRH)**, which stimulates the anterior **pituitary gland** to release one of its many hormones, called **adrenocorticotropic hormone (ACTH)**. This hormone causes the release of **glucocorticoids** into the bloodstream, one of which is **cortisol**, from the adrenal gland cortex located just on top of the kidneys.

This results in a number of effects that allow the body to better deal with stress, including raising the glucose level, enabling energy production necessary to deal with stress reduction.

Once the amount of cortisol present in the blood is high, negative feedback goes to the brain, resulting in the hypothalamus and the hippocampus stopping the production and releasing both hormones **(CRH, ACTH)**, stimulating the pituitary gland and the adrenal glands.

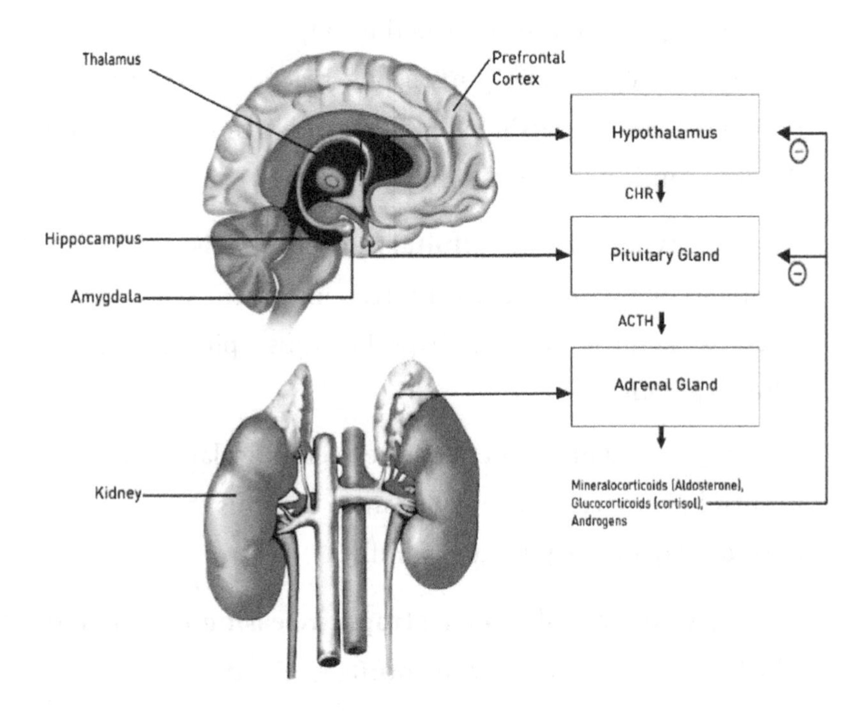

Figure 1: Shows some of the anatomical structures involved in stress and the hypothalamus-pituitary-adrenal axis.

Other vital structures in the process include the following:

The amygdala, like all the other parts of the brain, is complex. However, it is believed to have an essential function in emotion, behavior, fear, or perceived threat.

The hippocampus's primary role is associated with functional memory and learning.

The autonomic nervous system is part of the peripheral nervous system that involuntarily controls or regulates the physiologic processes of the body, such as the cardiovascular system, digestive system, respiration, and sexual arousal. It has three anatomic divisions: sympathetic, parasympathetic (two principal components), and enteric nervous system.

The sympathetic nervous system is responsible for preparing the body for the "fight or flight" (freeze or faint) response once an individual determines that there is a potential danger or a threat to them. Both **epinephrine (adrenaline) and norepinephrine (noradrenaline)** are essential hormones in the "flight or fight" response.

The **parasympathetic nervous system** is responsible for inhibiting the body's response to "fight or flight," preventing it from overworking and allowing it to return to its normal state, usually after the sympathetic nervous system was activated because of a potential threat.

The **enteric nervous system** also helps regulate and control the function of the digestive system. It is capable of acting independently of the sympathetic and parasympathetic nervous systems. It can operate independently of the brain and spinal cord but relies on innervation from the autonomic nervous system via the **vagus nerve** and paravertebral ganglia.

The **somatic nervous system** controls muscles and movement.

Oxytocin is produced by the hypothalamus and secreted by the posterior pituitary gland. In addition to being associated with milk production and involved in pregnancy and birth, it is also believed to be related to social bonding, trust, empathy, and stress. Furthermore, oxytocin is believed to be associated with behaviors such as aggression and negative emotions.

Endorphins are a group of hormones that are secreted within the brain and nervous system. They have and create a significant physiological function by acting on the body's opiate receptors. This has the potential to create a feeling of euphoria or well-being and/or pain reduction.

These are the body's natural opioids and respond similarly to exogenous opioids, prescribed or illegal. Endorphins are often released in response to pain or activities pleasurable or not, such as physical exercise or even eating or stress.

Serotonin is produced in the brain. It can be considered as one of our happy hormones. Serotonin plays many key roles in regulating or stabilizing many functions, such as our mood, appetite, digestion, and sleep. Conversely, low levels of serotonin are strongly associated with depression and anxiety.

Dopamine, a hormone, has some similarities to serotonin. It is produced in the brain. Some of its roles are regulation or the stabilization of mood, muscle movements, and modulating the brain's pleasure-reward system.

Melatonin is produced in the brain (pineal gland). It is believed to be associated with regulating the sleep cycle or the circadian rhythms in our body. Its levels are believed to be higher at night or when it is dark than during daylight.

It is essential to understand the critical association of stress with the brain's and body's anatomy and pathophysiology and how this correlation helps address some of the malfunctions or medical issues relating to structures or hormone imbalance. Therefore, it is crucial that signs and symptoms of stress are not just looked at as caused by stimuli from external or internal factors that are unrelated to anatomy or physiology. We should also consider and rule out medical causes. Hence, the presentation of some stress symptoms will need at the very least a medical evaluation to establish the appropriate cause. This may range from neurological, abnormal hormone levels, underlying psychiatric illnesses, and other factors affecting any aspect of the anatomical structures or the physiology involved in the manifestation or presentation of stress signs and symptoms.

CHAPTER 1C

Concepts of Stress Management

There are numerous factors that are involved in the management and treatment of stress or that may be helpful in some ways to prevent or reduce the levels experienced. Therefore, I have organized the different actions that will result in stress reduction into three broad categories, which I will call **Foster's Stress Action Plan**, as follows:

1. The **Physical Actions (PA)** that are required to reduce stress.
2. The **Mental Actions (MA)** that are required to reduce stress.
3. The **Community Actions (CA)** that are required to reduce stress.

These actions create the acronym P.A.M.A.C.A. The actions in each group may overlap. However, for simplicity, each group is defined as follows:

Physical Actions involve an individual who performs an action with limited mental effects on that person and is not necessarily significantly dependent on anyone else to make that decision. For example, if someone decides to install an alarm system in their home because they believe it will make them safer, that is a physical action, or similarly, if they chose to create a list of the factors that are causing them to be stressed.

Mental Actions are those that are primarily dependent on the individual that needs to take them. The result of taking these actions has the potential to create a significant or considerable emotional effect, negative or positive. For example, if someone decided to terminate their relationship with their partner, there may be significant emotional trauma or energy; perhaps, fear of their partner's reaction. Although ending the relationship is also performing a physical action, the more significant part of the process is dealing with the mental or emotional consequence of making that decision. Another example is having self-esteem issues. Although that may be related to other people in their lives, each person is still primarily responsible for assessing and evaluating themselves and how they feel.

Community Actions) involve an individual working or collaborating with others to reduce their stress. That is, performing activities that will include others that probably will result in stress level reduction. For example, the act of seeking medical or professional care involves the individual and other people involved in the process. Another example would be someone who is involved in a particular job, which will also include others as well.

Some actions will not necessarily fit into one category clearly, or they may appear to fit into more than one category. However, the actions that the stressed person needs to take are intended to help reduce stress. Therefore, if someone decides to use illegal drugs, for example, that person is committing an action that will have consequences that are likely to increase their stress levels, more so mentally than physically. Hence, not using illegal drugs would be considered an action to improve stress to be a mental action also since the options of drug use are choices to be made. Consequently, the category for illegal drug use would be mental action as opposed to physical action.

In understanding stress management, the best result is most likely to be obtained when all three categories are applied to manage or treat stress. Particularly when several stress factors contribute to an individual's stress level, if someone has minimum or low-level stress, it may not be critically necessary for all three categories of actions to be incorporated into their stress management protocol. However, in general, it will be more beneficial if all three categories' actions are used. All these categories are essential; however, the category of mental action will become more significant, particularly for those with mental disorders or other comorbidities that make it difficult for them to process things mentally. Our mind is the most central part of stress reduction and management.

So, utilizing the three actions in the management and treatment of stress is essential to realize that all are closely intertwined. Some of the activities or tasks required in each of these three Action Plans will have some overlaps between treatment plans when dealing with stress, particularly for chronic stress. Also, those with many stress factors that are often complicated by multiple comorbidities, multiple levels of psychosocial issues, economic issues, and a myriad of other things may find appropriate therapy less successful. The importance of the **Stress Action Plan** concept using physical, mental, and community actions will potentially result in better treatment outcomes. Each individual will get more lasting benefits by effectively reducing their level of stress.

Words of Caution or Comments

1. The impact of stress in our lives can take a significant toll that literally determines the extent to which we succeed.
2. A significant component of how well one responds to the management or treatment of stress will depend on an action plan that is practical and will improve stress levels. The **Foster's Stress Action Plan** will do just that. **Physical, Mental,** and **Community Actions** that are implemented using a direct approach will most likely result in improvement of the subject's stress level.

SECTION TWO

SOME NECESSARY *PHYSICAL ACTIONS* YOU NEED TO TAKE TO REDUCE YOUR STRESS LEVEL

CHAPTER 2

Identify Your Stressors and the Reasons Why You Are Stressed

One of the first things to do concerning stress management is identify the stressors or factors causing you to be stressed. Then, once you have recognized these factors, write them down. The moment you write them down, things will start to fall into place because now you have a physical and mental picture of what is in front of you, what you need to do, when things should be done, and what is essential.

Each of you will have a list that is likely to be different from each other. For example, the list may include financial concerns, toxic relationships, unresolved medical issues, taking on more responsibilities or tasks than you can complete in a reasonable time, family or relationship conflicts, divorce, job performance, environmental factors, a challenging social or personal life, fear of not meeting your obligations, the need to meet deadlines, trying to keep up with others, the fear of missing out—a never-ending list of things.

Make sure that you put them in order of importance by prioritizing them. Make sure you understand which is a priority or needs to be dealt with now, even if not necessarily in the order of importance; you have to consider the timeline of these problems. If you have something that is very important but does not require fulfillment or will come to a resolution in a month or two months from now, you should not use most of your time necessarily trying to complete that task now. This does not mean that you should not do anything about it, but it should not entirely consume you now. Work on it but focus more on what needs to be done right now or a very short time from now. In other words, your priority should not be only driven by the importance of the tasks to be completed but also the time frame or the timeline you have.

The concept of prioritizing tasks is an essential one required in goal setting. Keep this in mind when you read chapter 3.

Sometimes after compiling a list like this or whatever you plan to address, the thought of completing the tasks identified can be overwhelming and indeed stressful. However, even though that may be the case, it is still imperative to make a complete list of all the things you consider to be contributing to your stress. Also include those things that you think may, to some degree, be of limited impact on your life. Do this as soon as possible.

Regarding the importance of the timeline, let me tell you about Big Joe, who had a house that he was trying to sell that needed some specialized repair work completed. He hoped to get his house on the market within a week. Big Joe also had his personal home, which required an electric socket to be installed, which can often be done relatively quickly. However, there was no immediate need or urgency for its installation. The person who did the job had one day to spare because he was from out of town. Because the job at the personal home was presumed to be small, Big Joe had the worker start there. However, the worker had difficulty installing the socket because the wiring required much more extensive work, cutting walls and running additional wires than initially planned. In addition to that, repairing the wall after the wiring was completed had to be done. This consumed the worker's entire day, and he never got to the house that needed to be repaired in preparation for sale. It took Big Joe another six to eight weeks to find someone to do the specialized job at the house for sale.

The point here is that awareness of your priorities is fundamental in knowing how to utilize your time in the order of importance. The consequences of not being able to have planned actions ready to be implemented can sometimes be costly. Clearly, it would have been wiser if the worker had completed the priority job rather than starting at Big Joe's home.

We often function like a computer or smartphone where we will have many files or applications open simultaneously while we are only using only one or a few. Therefore, it is essential to temporarily close those open files that we are not using or have no intention of using and focus on the essentials of the task.

Table: To Help You Identify and Find Solutions for Your Stress Factors

STRESSORS (What is causing stress?)	TIME (Period for resolution?)	REASONS (Why are you stressed?)	EMERGENCY (Which stressor is highest priority?)	SOLUTIONS (What solutions are available to solve stressors ?)	SUPPORT (Who can help provide resources for solution?)
JOB-RELATED					
FINANCIAL					
PROBLEMATIC RELATIONSHIPS CHILD/PARTNER					
COMMUNITY ACTIVITIES					
EDUCATIONAL ACTIVITIES					
HEALTH CONCERN					
YOUR OWN					

Table 1. Foster's S.T.R.E.S.S. Action Plan Table

The table above shows a basic stress action plan.

The acronym **S.T.R.E.S.S.** in this:

S - represents stress factors

T - represents projected time frame to resolve or improve the stress you are experiencing

R - represents the reasons why you're feeling stress

E - represents emergency, which is a ranking of which level of stressor or stress factor needs emergency attention or is a top priority

S - represents the solutions that can be applied to resolve or improve the stress, and

S - represents the supports that are available or which should be sought to help in removing or reducing the level of stress.

The categories chosen in the table are not specific to any one person. You get to choose and decide what factors are causing your stress. However, the same principle will apply by using the acronym **S.T.R.E.S.S.** for each stress factor. The next helpful application of this acronym is to use it in conjunction with the goals you have set and established. (See goal setting in the next chapter.)

Let us look at an example of an application with the stress factor "educational activities":

Consider Mary, a busy divorced mother with two kids, one boy of ten years old and one girl of fourteen, who are active in afterschool activities. Mary, while working full-time, is taking courses at the local community college to become a registered nurse; she is very close to graduation. Her ex-husband provides occasional financial support for the children, resulting in Mary taking him to court for child support payments as she struggles to pay the bills.

Mary also relies on her friends and neighbors to help with chauffeuring her children from afterschool activities. Her daughter stays at home with her younger brother until Mary gets home. Mary is concerned because her daughter is not doing well in school. She is not sure precisely what is wrong with her but is hoping to find out somehow.

In this scenario, Mary can check most of the boxes in the table. However, she really wants to resolve the stress related to her educational activities. Therefore, a detailed plan for her may look something like this:

S: Educational activities

T: Need to be resolved in three months

R: She will have to repeat her courses and may not be able to graduate. In addition, she will have to wait another year. Last year she repeated some courses. Now she is not sure whether she will have to drop out of the program completely

E: Mary has made her educational activities her main priority that must be addressed despite all the other stressors that others may consider more important.

S: (Solution)

1. How far behind is Mary in her studies?
2. Can tutoring help her at this time?
3. How will she pay for tutoring?

4. Will she be eligible to continue if she fails to complete her course if she stops now?

How are the other stress factors impacting her? What can be done to reduce some of the effects of other stressors that she does not consider priorities right now?

S: (Support)

1. Meeting with a counselor at the community college might be helpful
2. What are other possible financial resources for Mary?
3. Is it reasonable for her to take a break from the educational activities at this time and resume them sometime in the near future?
4. Are there other stress factors that may be more important than the educational factor that seems less important at this time to Mary?
5. Can Mary afford professional help other than the counselor at the community college?
6. Does Mary have any family members who may be able to help her?
7. Are there any non-profit or civic groups that might be able to provide some assistance?

As you can see, these problems and their solutions have various options, and they are not always simple or easy. That is in part one of the reasons why it is so difficult to deal with stress. Very often, the vast majority of people who do have stress do not just have one issue. They have multiple issues that compound the problems and, therefore, aggravate the stress level they are experiencing. Application of **Foster's Stress Action Plan** consisting of physical, mental, and community actions **(P.A.M.A.C.A.)** will be helpful. No one likes stress, and no one wants to experience the feeling associated with stress. Therefore, whatever treatment or management protocol that is offered will require a change from doing whatever you are doing to something else that will improve your stress level. Therefore, you must change. The famous poet and author Maya Angelou put it this way:

> "If you don't like something, change it. If you can't change it, change your attitude." — Maya Angelou[48,49]

Words of Caution or Comments

1. In this book, you will find some ideas and solutions that will put you in a preventative mode that is so much better than trying to resolve many of these problems that will invariably present themselves regardless of the position that you may be in.
2. Solutions and support in stress **(S.T.R.E.S.S.)** management are very closely related and may have significant overlaps. Both are essential in the effective management of stress.

CHAPTER 3

Set Goals for Each Day of Your Life. Plan Your Day, Plan Your Life

One of the essential things that is extremely helpful in managing stress is goal setting, which is part of almost every self-help guide that emphasizes the need to improve one's life. Besides generic reasons for setting goals, it is crucial to set goals with specific objectives or rationales. Understanding the reasons or specific desire to set goals can and will be significant motivating factors that will be the driving force in determining whether certain goals are achieved.

Furthermore, setting goals generally gives you direction and a purpose of what to do next and what is essential. What are the potential obstacles that must be overcome, and what are the supporting factors or resources that are likely to be helpful? What skills or expertise will you need to accomplish your goals? And finally, who has the skills or expertise that you need? Regardless of the purpose of setting goals, you will essentially be creating a road map for the path that you intend to take to accomplish the tasks you have at hand. Whether your goal is personal, business, social, or professionally related, you will find goal-setting helpful. This is definitely one of the critical components of reducing stress in anyone's life. All the people around you will be helped by you being more focused and more direct in your approach to accomplishing the various objectives you have set.

Your goals should be written down; they should be thoroughly thought out, and you should be able to access these readily for review as necessary. You should also assess the progress you make in your effort to accomplish each goal that you set.

One of the main objectives of goal-setting is that the process puts things in perspective and creates a sense of priority of what is essential and what needs to be done in a specific order. This often requires establishing a timetable of what things need to be accomplished at a particular time, albeit sometimes generalized. Still, it will allow you to have a better perspective of when you need to do things instead of just thinking about something that does not need to be done now. Setting goals will help you think about things that should be done way in advance and in the short term.

The concept of prioritizing tasks is an essential one required in goal setting and is discussed in Chapter 2.

Having goals allows you to visualize and create a future of reality out of possibilities. Here is what Tony Robbins, author, and motivational speaker, and Robert F. Smith, philanthropist, and businessman, have to say about goals and vision:

> "Setting goals is the first step into turning the invisible into the visible." – Tony Robbins[39,48]

> "Have the vision of what you want to become, but you have to put consistent action behind that vision in order for that to manifest, and it has to be consistent." — Robert F. Smith[65,66]

An acronym for goal setting called S.M.A.R.T., developed by a former Director of Corporate Planning for Washington Water Power Company, George Doran, et al., reported in a 1981 article, is often used. Some people may find it helpful to varying degrees. These letters stand for:

S, which means that your goals should be specific;

M, for measurable;

A, that your goals should be achievable;

R, that your goals should be realistic; and

T, that your goals should be timely or should have a time frame in which they should be accomplished.

Besides having personal goals, it is essential to have goals for whatever else you are doing in life. For example, if you are involved in an organization and a part of the executive team or board, that organization should also have goals. It is incumbent on you to know and understand the organization's goals and objectives so that you can help facilitate those goals. This will make the organization much better and reduce the amount of stress you and the other team members may have concerning the organization's role.

Similarly, if you are employed and have a job or you are volunteering, or whatever you are doing, there should be established goals to help you. If you are at your job, you should not just go there and sit around without any objectives of what needs to be accomplished. It is essential to know and understand your company's goals and objectives, specifically your role, and what goals you have to complete to be a productive worker or a productive member of the team regardless of your employment level. This will allow you to be a more efficient and valuable employee or a resource for your company or the organization you serve. In addition, if everyone in the company is working to achieve those goals, your job will likely become less stressful.

This simple concept applies to almost any organization or whatever else you are trying to accomplish. It is always important to know your company's specific objectives so that when you are working on them or trying to achieve what is required of you, you can establish a realistic time frame in which they can be completed.

Or, if not, are you working on something that probably is not likely to be realized? If you are aware of these things, then your contribution can be much more helpful. You will likely be more motivated to accomplish the tasks at hand and be beneficial to your fellow co-workers or associates. Similarly, if you're in business, or a professional, or in some other entity, your partners will greatly benefit if you understand and become an active participant in attaining the established goals. Clearly, an essential part of this is you being a significant contributor to stress reduction through your involvement in implementing goals or being the facilitator for seeing these goals accomplished.

Once you establish these goals, it is crucial to understand all the obstacles that may prevent you from achieving them. How will you ensure that these obstacles are removed or overcome? It will be incumbent on you to monitor these goals so that they are not just sitting there and you are failing to measure the progress that is being made. This may be a point where a timetable might help you establish deadlines for each goal you have set. Also helpful is establishing a process of achieving your goals and knowing what you need to do each day to ensure that your activities are consistent with the goals you are trying to accomplish. That will take you into establishing immediate goals, short-term goals, and long-term goals. John C. Maxwell, author, and public speaker, said:

> "You'll never change your life until you change something you do daily. The secret of your success is found in your daily routine." – John C. Maxwell[15,39]

Evaluating and re-evaluating the process should be a regular part of the assessment as you strive to reach your goals.

Here is an example of a worksheet:

Name ______________________________________

Specific-Goal

____

____

Date Started __________ Projected End Date__________

(Incorporate each day into your action plan for your goal)

Specific methods or criteria to assess progress and attainment of the goal

List at least five actions you will take to attain your goal:

1.

2.

3.

4.

5.

List possible obstacles or challenges to accomplishing the goal and how to overcome them.

List possible sources of help or individuals who may help you accomplish your goal. Include them in your action plan.

The following is a list of some essential things that should be included on any basic worksheet for goals:

1. List of immediate goals
2. List of short-term goals
3. List of long-term goals
4. Obstacles to overcome
5. Ways of overcoming obstacles
6. Who can help?
7. Where to go for help?
8. Why is this goal important?
9. How will I measure my progress?
10. How long will it take to achieve?
11. Is this goal achievable or realistic?

Finally, regardless of how hard we try to make our goals become a reality, there is often something that makes our achievement more difficult. This is a natural part of our development and growth. Anything worthwhile does not come easy. One thing that will be important to you and your overall plan and goal setting will be the need for you to incorporate a **Plan B Action** in case **Plan A Action** does not materialize. This is important not just for potentially long-term and short-term goals but also for your day-to-day activities. It doesn't have to be a significant decision in general. But let's say, for example, you are working on a home project. You are depending on someone to show up to help you complete it—Plan A. If the person doesn't show up then, Plan B might be to get someone else lined up before the project's start date. Or you may need to be prepared to postpone the task for another day. Just by having that mindset, you are creating less stress on yourself.

What about something more significant than a simple project? For example, what if your fiancé didn't show up for your wedding? You might not have a good immediate Plan B unless you thought about that possibility ahead of your wedding. And if you did, you probably should not have been involved in that marriage in the first place. This is more complex and more difficult. However, despite the challenges or disappointments, you may face from things not going your way and having a Plan B option or an alternative action plan can make a significant difference in the level of stress you potentially could face. Where possible or necessary, always try to implement planning into your general daily goal settings or objectives. Whatever you do to reduce stress in your life is a critical factor in creating a more manageable and adjusted life, particularly when you have a plan in place instead of just trying to make it up as you go along.

A real-life story: A lesson of focus and determination to achieve a specific goal.

The importance of being focused on getting things done is essential in your growth and development. However, sometimes you have to do all you can to ensure that others do not facilitate or determine the likelihood of your success or cause your failure by their action or inaction. I want to tell you a story about Mr. River.

Mr. River is an appraiser of real estate properties. He pulled up to a gated community where the security guard on duty required him to get out of his vehicle and bring his ID to their counter, about six feet away. However, he decided he would not do that because he has a health condition that makes it difficult for him to get in and out of his vehicle easily. The security personnel decided they were not getting out of their security booth to collect his ID about six feet away from his truck. Mr. River called the homeowner and stated what was happening. The homeowner called the security guard, and they essentially said the same thing, emphasizing that they are required to remain in their booth. The homeowner was about a mile away from the security gate. He had to get in his vehicle, go to the security gate, collect the ID from Mr. River, give it to the security guard, collect an electronic pass from the security guard, and give it to Mr. River. Mr. River was allowed into the premises and completed the appraisal of the homeowner's properties. The homeowner got what he needed to be done.

The point here is that neither of the two people, the security guard, and Mr. Rivers, were willing to move from their seated position to a distance of literally less than six feet to resolve a simple issue that would affect the homeowner adversely. However, the homeowner decided that he would stop what he was doing and drove to the gate to make this process that he needed to be completed a reality. So to emphasize, although you have people who take whatever action, have whatever agenda, or are experiencing whatever in their life, sometimes having nothing to do with you, you should never let their action impact you adversely. The homeowner, in this case, needed that appraisal done within a specific timeframe and had a lot financially relying on its completion. Therefore he could not allow the appraiser to drive away, resulting in further delay and a negative impact.

There are times when you may have to take all the steps necessary to accomplish what you need, even though sometimes it is at your inconvenience or things are really silly or crazy. You have to see a bigger picture of what you are trying to accomplish and take those extra steps to ensure that you get what you want to get done, done. Regardless of the consequences, as long as it is legitimate and doesn't hurt other people or affect them adversely, then go ahead. Without getting the important things you need to be accomplished, your life will be more stressed and challenged by failures of letting other people derail you from your primary objectives, even if they have no idea of the impact or consequences of their actions.

Finally, it is so critically important to understand that when setting goals, although it is a significant part of life's achievements and stress management, doing so alone will not be effective or productive unless you have concrete and strategic plans to obtain the goals that you have set. Unless we create the processes and mechanisms to achieve these goals and effectively implement them, setting goals will become almost meaningless.

Words of Caution or Comments

1. Always determine your priorities in life, and never forget to treat them that way.
2. Priorities will give your life purpose, give your life meaning, and help you to focus on the things that matter most. This will definitely reduce the level of stress that you experience or contribute to others.

3. You are the CEO of your life, you are on a mission, and you must have the goals and vision to take you to your ultimate destination.
4. Without goals and a vision that is consistent with your mission, you do not determine your destiny; others do.
5. Understanding our vision and incorporating it into our lives' dreams is one of the driving forces that allows us to succeed. The ability to see and believe things before they happen is often one of the many things that distinguish those that are successful from those that are not.
6. Create your mission and vision statements and along with your goals, let them be part of your life's journey.

And when you make your goals and create your dreams, take a few words from Joel Osteen, an American pastor, televangelist, businessperson, and author:

> "Your dream may look impossible, but God said blessings will chase you down. Ask big. Take the limits off of God." — Joel Osteen.[39,40]

7. Share your goals, dreams, and aspirations with your partner or those who mean you well. This makes the journey of life that you take more rewarding.
8. Goal setting is an essential part of stress management. It will allow you to be more focused and self-directed in accomplishing not only minor tasks but major ones that will ultimately move you closer to the vision of your life.

CHAPTER 4

Budget Your Money

Money or finances are often considered among the significant factors that are important in every aspect of life. There is no doubt that its importance correlates well with stress. There is a significant association between money and stress; sometimes it is the lack of money, insufficient funds, or having too much money, and all the associated challenges.

Sometimes it's misusing money or simply being consumed by it to the degree that nothing else matters. We have heard it said that there are people who will do anything and everything for money. This often leads to destructive behaviors, sometimes crimes, causing harm to others or themselves. In some ways, all of these are related to stress, and the consequences of living a stressful life that is compounded by the desire to acquire money or the belief of what having money will ultimately bring.

Having a budget is undoubtedly one of the surest ways of reducing the stress level you might experience. But, of course, it will not solve all of your financial problems. Still, it will provide you with a framework of understanding that will help you navigate some of the economic challenges that have led to the stress you may be experiencing.

Everyone should have a budget of how they will spend and keep some of their earnings and do everything possible to live within its limits. Managing finances is always one of those critical and essential elements in everyone's life. You do not want to go over your budget, or at the very least, you need to exercise some control of where your funds are going. It does not matter how much you have or how much you think that you don't have. We all should have a budget.

A budget is an objective plan (an estimate) of how you will spend your money or use your earnings (income) for services or goods (expenses) for a given period.

There are many key factors in establishing a budget. Among them are: how much income do you earn, how much do you spend, what objects and services constitute your expenses, and over what time frame? Each of you will have similar but different line items for each product or service that is part of your expenses. Clearly, the amount you spend on any given product or service will be different, as well as your income and expenditure. Some people may be living in poverty without much income, unemployed, or on disability. Some will have low income while others will have substantial income or earnings so that, for the most part, a budget doesn't make a lot of difference to them, although it will be important in general.

There are several ways to create a budget. One could begin by simply writing down their income and expenses for a time frame.

Then examine and see how much funds are leftover, if any, and determine what purpose that amount could be used for, for example, for savings. Or simply cut or reduce the budget to avoid a negative balance.

Ensure that you can determine what expenses are a priority and necessary versus those that are less important and probably could be removed from the budget, or the amount allocated could be reduced.

Regardless of what you do, always try to avoid spending more than you are earning. Failure to do that is almost a guarantee that your budget will never be balanced. Therefore, it will be literally impossible for you to save any of your income for future use. Sometimes it is extremely challenging to have a balanced budget, particularly when your income is low.

Napoleon Hill, an American self-help author, said it best:

> "Tell me how you use your spare time, and how you spend your money, and I will tell you where and what you will be in ten years from now." — Napoleon Hill.[69,70]

However, regardless of the size of your income, remember that you can also get financial counseling to guide you directly in dealing with some of these issues. In addition, there are many books on the subject of budgeting and finance. There are also numerous computer programs or software and smartphone applications that can be utilized to create a budget. I encourage you to research them and find out which one is most suitable for your needs.[97] One of the primary goals of having a budget is to allow you to live within your means. Former President Calvin Coolidge understood this:

> "There is no dignity quite so impressive and no independence quite so important as living within your means." — President Calvin Coolidge.[15,101]

Digital Currency – Cryptocurrency

As the world becomes more computerized every day, the financial landscape is changing rapidly. The way we do business or conduct financial transactions is changing radically in front of our eyes. Most of us are familiar with credit card transactions. We literally do not have to have a paper trail; everything can be done electronically: we can pay electronically and get a receipt electronically. The banking system is gradually becoming entirely digitally ready as we all move into the future, with or without you.

The increased level of stress that is likely to come with digital currency is very evident with cryptocurrency. Digital currency as a whole is expected to be regulated or centralized, whereas cryptocurrency, which is a form of digital currency, is currently not regulated by governmental agencies in general. For the most part, it is a decentralized process giving almost complete control of all assets or cryptocurrencies to the participants or owners with few exceptions.[99,100] This and other factors, in part, tend to create a high level of stress with owning cryptocurrencies, trading, and safeguarding them.

The trading of cryptocurrencies is clearly not for those unable to tolerate extreme levels of stress. Trading can create extreme stress levels and frustration resulting in significant financial loss or gain or somewhere in between. A substantial part of the stress is directly related to the incredible volatility of the cryptocurrency trading market, which makes the traditional stock market look and feels like child's play. A terrible day for trading in traditional stocks may be a drop in the market of two to five percent of the value of stocks traded on a given day. However, in cryptocurrency trading, it is very common to see a percentage change from five to thirty-plus percent in a given day of the value of the total currencies traded. This is seen in trading in the market as a whole, and individual cryptocurrency changes almost daily. Therefore, it is critical that you have done your research and understand what you are doing if you choose to jump into the cryptocurrency market. You may even consider joining one or more of the many related groups on the various social media platforms. However, as the saying goes: only invest what you can afford to lose (read more in protecting your cryptocurrency in chapter 7) and always stay within your budget.

Finally, not only are individual investors, and speculators stressed regarding digital/cryptocurrency but also anyone who has a significant career commitment in the traditional financial world. The future is changing rapidly and is very unpredictable.

The following is a basic monthly budget worksheet:

MONTHLY BUDGET				
ITEMS EXPENSES	BUDGET AMOUNT	ACTUALLY SPENT	DIFFERENCE	COMMENTS
Rent/mortgage				
Electricity				
Gas/oil				
Telephone/Internet				
Cell phone				
Cable service				
Charity/donation/tides				
Water				
Groceries				
Health insurance				
Laundries and supplies				
Car payment				
Lawn care				
Car insurance				
Travel - gas/toll/train				
Babysitters/childcare				
Educational expense				
Entertainment				
Savings				
TOTAL EXPENSES				
TOTAL INCOMES – Salary, Child Support, Alimony, Others				
BALANCE				

Table: Basic Example of Budget Plan – each person's items listed will vary.

Words of Caution or Comments

1. In constructing a budget, consider your income or earnings and your expenses and consider making an effort to save.[97]
2. Make saving an essential part of any budget you make, regardless of how difficult this may be. This will allow you to at least prepare for the future, which may include possible emergencies.
3. Sometimes, producing a budget can be stressful; however, the overall benefits outweigh the risks of not having one. Understanding what your financial boundaries are and living within limits are crucial criteria necessary for any budget to work.
4. Make sure your budget has objectives that fit within your overall goals of what you are trying to accomplish, not just for now but for your long-term and short-term goals.
5. Finally, be flexible and be willing to make sacrifices to achieve your desired outcome. You and your stress level will be better off for it.

CHAPTER 5

Exercise Your Body, Your Mind, and Your Stomach

Exercise Your Body

As important as exercise is in so many different ways, this chapter aims not to describe the different types of exercises, how they should be performed, or the benefits and disadvantages of doing one exercise over another. The main focus of this chapter is to highlight the benefits of exercise with respect to stress.

Physical exercise is one of the main stress-relieving activities that anyone can do. Therefore, it is essential to ensure that the amount of exercise you get is adequate.

Exercise has many vital benefits to the human body as well as the mind. These include general strengthening and conditioning, which improves the cardiovascular system. This will also lead to increased blood flow, causing an increase in oxygen supply to the various parts of our body that need it to function. Exercise performed over time and consistently will improve blood pressure and heart disease, lower cholesterol levels, decrease weight gain, and improve conditions of many other related medical issues.

Concerning stress, exercise increases endorphins, which are the body's natural opiates. These hormones have the potential to create a feeling of well-being as well as provide some pain relief. Therefore, exercise is one of the most significant things that almost anyone can do to improve their overall stress level.

There are many different types of exercises. These may include: aerobic exercise, exercise using stationary or free weights, exercise by walking, and jogging or running. There are also exercises such as tai chi, which combines movements and relaxation, Pilates exercise, Zumba dancing, other forms of dancing, and many other exercises. Including deep breathing exercises and relaxation techniques that are also helpful in modulating stress.

Just about all exercises will increase the level of endorphins and the level of cortisol to different degrees. Both of these hormones and several others are important in helping overall to decrease the level of stress.

In general, we should exercise our body about three to five times per week for about half-hour to an hour. The U.S. Department of Health and Human Services suggested guidelines is that for moderate to active adults, the target range of activity should be between 150 minutes to 300 minutes of moderate physical exercise activity per week. However, for highly active adults, 75 minutes of vigorous activity or its equivalent combination is recommended to meet the target range. Highly active is doing the equivalent of more than 300 minutes of moderate-intensity physical activity a week. [111]

It is essential to make sure that your medical provider clears you before you start any exercise program. Exercising without being medically capable can lead to catastrophic outcomes. This is extremely important, regardless of how healthy you might think you are. Once you have obtained medical clearance, you can enjoy your exercise knowing that you will be a much happier and safer person. In addition, you will have less stress performing those exercises and be healthier, with higher energy levels, improving your chance of decreasing chronic illnesses, improving your brain function, and your mind.

Exercise Your Mind

Now in as much as we exercise our body, we should also exercise our mind because it is the most important of the many factors that control our stress level. We need to exercise our minds to be better equipped for the many challenges we all will face. Our mind is our computer, and we are the gatekeepers of what we allow to be uploaded to it. Whatever we put in our minds is what drives it or allows it to function. If we put negative thoughts in our minds, then those are the main focus. It will then have no other choice but to use the information, process it, and generate results consistent with the information we upload. We will see this showing up in our actions, moods, various malfunctions of the body, or manifestation of other disease processes and a myriad of other health-related conditions and behaviors.

So, it is critically important that you feed your minds with inspirational and good thoughts and make sure that you fill your mind with essential things for your development and growth. Ensure that you take time to meditate because the mind is the most precious tool we have.

Lao Tzu, also known as Laozi and Lao-Tze, was a Chinese philosopher who summarized as follows:

> "Watch your thoughts, they become your words; watch your words, they become your actions; watch your actions, they become your habits; watch your habits, they become your character; watch your character, it becomes your destiny." — Lao Tzu.[15,71]

There are many different types of meditations, including Transcendental Meditations, which are believed to lead to a higher plane of our state of awareness. There are also Mindfulness types of meditations, which focus on how one fits in with their environment. Some individuals may also benefit from Yoga, which combines exercises and meditation, and Qigong, which affects the flow of energy or Qi and different channels or meridians of our body. These types of meditations and/or exercises and others facilitate the mind to better cope with the effects of stress on the body as a whole.

Be careful what you allow in your mind. We are in an environment where there are so many things that can gain access to our minds if we let them. There is news, information, and entertainment from all various sources—radio, television, social media, print media—all reaching us simultaneously. In addition to these, we have those who we allow to be close to us—friends, groups, community organizations, religious groups, groups with their own agenda. The list is endless.

It is our solemn responsibility and interest to know and understand that we have control over what goes into our minds. And that we should never ever relinquish that to anyone, any group, or any entity. Because once we do that, we no longer have control of ourselves. It is a well-known fact that once we gravitate towards something, whether that be a group or an idea, then that entity or idea often becomes more acceptable to us. We have seen in the media and social platforms where once we start paying attention to a particular thing, then that is what we are fed continuously. For example, if we conduct a search on the internet for carpets, the next time we visit that platform and others, we will see several solicitations about carpets. Suppose we appear to support a political party or a group, or a particular country. In that case, anything related to that country or those things will be what is shown to us repeatedly. Now, that may be good selling and advertising for those who are trying to get us to subscribe to their ideas. But that also often limits some of us from expanding our knowledge and capacity to see other things. These include things that are different, other important things, or things that we may not have thought about simply because we are now so focused on the limited content that the people who are watching us want us to see.

We have to allow ourselves to break away from that mind control mechanism. Because not only does it reduce or limit us to what they want us to be, but it also creates a slew of people essentially with blinders on, potentially filled with so much stress, making them unable to deal effectively with the broader community outside of an artificially created comfort zone. Take off those blinders and limit your exposure to some of these influences on your minds, or at the very least understand their impact on you. Allow yourself to see the broader picture of the world and the numerous possibilities we can all be a part of. Aristotle, a Greek philosopher, said:

> "We are what we repeatedly do. Excellence, then, is not an act, but a habit." — Aristotle.[15,44]

One may also utilize environmental therapy (using nature or the surroundings and its benefit), pet therapy, or different games to stimulate the brain. Also helpful are other forms of therapy such as reading, having stimulating conversations filled with laughter, and listening to music.

The Right Diet for Our Body and Our Mind

We spoke about exercising our mind or feeding our mind with inspirational thoughts or good thoughts. It's also essential to exercise our stomach by providing it with the right foods or the proper nutrients, creating a balanced diet. This allows our body to be nourished appropriately. To function at our best, we need the right foods or nutrients to function effectively. So, we should make sure that whatever we put in our mouth is balanced and is good. Some foods will change our mood while others will change our bodies acutely, and some will change it over time. Therefore, it is extremely essential that we have an appropriate diet or a balanced diet critical to our well-being and development. Eating well is also necessary as it relates to stress. Simply put, whatever we put in our mouths will be reflected in our bodies and may also affect our minds.

There are numerous publications about diet and nutrition. This section of the book is not intended to provide you with specific information about the different types of diets that will be beneficial and helpful with stress directly. Instead, it's intended to let you be aware of the association or correlation between your diet and stress. I encourage you to make every effort to familiarize yourself with different types of foods or nutrients that can and will affect your mood and potentially cause your stress level to be elevated.

Another factor that can and will exacerbate stress related to diet and nutrition is that often when people are going through stress or difficult times, they may also have other mood-related symptoms or disorders. These may include, for example, anxiety or depression. This can result in them overindulging or overeating certain foods or food in general. These may involve excesses of carbohydrates or sugar, fat, and sometimes alcohol, to name a few, potentially resulting in negative consequences.

When you research foods or nutrients that will help decrease stress, be aware that this may be very confusing because of the lack of consistency in various publications. Some of this has to do with limited research and the many challenges of designing valid studies that can generate meaningful scientific data leading to sound conclusions.

Inventor and businessman Thomas Edison said:

> "The doctor of the future will no longer treat the human frame with drugs, but rather will cure and prevent disease with nutrition." — Thomas Edison.[44,84]

Words of Caution or Comments

1. Understanding the brain's pathophysiology and anatomy is also crucial to understanding the importance of good nutrition and diet regarding our bodies and minds. This relationship is discussed in Chapter 1B, The Anatomy of Stress.

2. We must always be careful of what we feed our bodies, ensuring we have the right and appropriate nutrients, ensuring that we take care of our beautiful minds and bodies.
3. We must remove negative emotions from our minds. We must learn how to let go of emotions such as hate, anger, self-criticism, emptiness, helplessness, fear, guilt, inadequacy, disgust, or sadness.
4. Take great care to cherish your positive thoughts and know that you have the power to determine what you allow your mind to focus on.
5. Let it be one of your most important quests in life, always to cherish, nourish, and develop your mind, not only to be prepared to face life's toughest challenges but also to allow you to thoroughly and completely enjoy all that life has to offer.
6. Letting go of negative emotions also gives us the power of forgiveness for others and ourselves.

CHAPTER 6

Make Time for Yourself, the Ones You Love and Those That Love You

Make Time for Yourself

The journey of life for some people is a slow walk. For others, it's a sprint, and for some, it is somewhere in between. But for most people, life is a marathon. It really does not matter how fast or how slow we run or whether we want to stop along the way or make a detour. However, what is extremely important is that we do our best to finish the race, regardless of the destination we have chosen. Also, it is essential to know that we have the option to determine to what extent we want to participate, but whatever our decisions are, the race of life continues. Therefore, some of us have a tendency to decide or try to figure out what is best for us and how we should proceed in the race of our lives. During this process, we put an undue amount of stress on ourselves to compete against whoever or whatever we perceive to be our competitors or threats. We try to climb the ladder of success and sometimes get to a point where we feel comfortable, at which point some of us stop while others continue trying to get to whatever point they believe to be the pinnacle of their lives.

These actions sometimes put us on what could best be described as "the treadmill," creating what I call **The Treadmill Syndrome**. This is essentially where your life and actions parallel being on a treadmill, but in this case, you cannot get off quickly or at will. You do not want to stop; sometimes, you cannot stop because you do not control the off button, and the only thing you know is that you have to keep going. Because if you stop or get off, you will miss something, or other people will be getting things you should benefit from. Interestingly enough, most of you will wake up one day and find that the treadmill is going nowhere even though you are moving and using all the energy that you can to keep up with all the others that are on with you. There is a sense that somehow you are accomplishing something and stopping is not an option.

The sad thing is that as you stress yourself through this process, you will finish your job or responsibility for the day with just enough time to go home to care for your family or yourselves and start the process all over again the next day. This usually occurs without any time for you to even think about what you are doing, why you are doing whatever it is, or if there are other options. Or, should you continue what you are doing? Or should you simply get off the treadmill regardless of the consequences?

Another important thing is that we often continue on the treadmill feeling that there is no need to get off, particularly when working on some things we believe are our 'stuff.' That may be our own company or our project or task, which we invested a lot in, and we feel that we shouldn't stop. Regardless, we should take time and get off the treadmill. This may require rescheduling appointments, canceling appointments, and letting people you are committed to know that you cannot fulfill your responsibility. However, these are not necessarily easy decisions that sometimes require you to take control of your life and reduce the various stressors and pressures that affect you even though you yourself are responsible for creating some of those factors. Sometimes it is essential to do these things to simply reduce the stress level you are experiencing and give yourself a chance to be better at whatever you're required to do in life.

We were fortunate enough to see an excellent example of this in the Tokyo Olympics (2020) in women's gymnastics, where the greatest female gymnast of all time, Simone Biles, hit the pause button for her mental health on one of the biggest stages of her life. Her action should remind us that we can say yes to ourselves even if it requires all the courage we have.[112,113]

Having said that, you probably wonder what about the idea of never giving up or not quitting? To that, I say that regardless of the degree of success or triumphs we have in our lives, we all have limits. (See the section in Chapter 19 - Everyone Has Limits). The difficulty we often face is differentiating when we are running on empty versus when our minds or we let others tell us that we have reached our limit. At that point, it is so critically important that we know and understand our support structures, enabling us to make the right decisions to carry on or when to crush the pause buttons of our lives.

Some of the greatest tragedies and failures in our lives come from the inability to know when to hit our pause buttons. This may often lead to self-inflicted physical and mental trauma requiring prolonged recovery and sometimes long-term management of the conditions that we created that could have been prevented.

Make sure that you get some rest or sometimes just sleep or take time and do nothing. Other times, you just need to step away from your life's activities and take a break regardless of how important they are or appear to be. It is so critical; you will need a break to regenerate or reinvigorate yourself. It will make a difference in terms of your performance and what you are doing. Take a break and get some adequate sleep, usually recommended about seven to eight hours per day. This is another essential thing that you need to do to improve your stress level. Legendary country singer-songwriter-actress Dolly Parton said it best:

> "Don't get so busy making a living that you forget to make a life." — Dolly Parton.[15,81]

Having balance in what we do in our life is essential. Otherwise, you go home with little or no energy or vigor for yourself or anyone else. This is, in part, a significant contribution to your stress level. It is so critically important that you simply take some time to rest. Get off the treadmill sometimes.

Make Time for the Ones You Love and Those That Love You

As important as it is to earn a living, support yourself and your family, be involved in civic organizations, charitable work, and doing all the things you want to do and things you like, you sometimes have to stop or pause. You have to stop and take stock of what you are doing and what you're accomplishing. It goes back to being on the treadmill, where you are busy doing everything, but you are not getting anywhere fast or slow. Sometimes, it may be hanging out with your friends, business partners, or professional colleagues, all or some of which may have important roles in your life. But there will come a time when you have to ask yourself if you have given all you have to others, what is left for your family and those you love and those who love you?

You have to structure your life and activities so that your family and the ones you love also get some of the quality time you spend with others. You should be able to have a meal without looking at your smartphone. Why do you need your laptop everywhere that you go? You should be able to ensure that there is enough quality time for you and your family to enjoy.

Every busy, productive person will have deadlines, have projects to complete, have reports to write, have places to go, and people to meet. However, this should not preclude you from making time for your family and loved ones. Relationship counsellor-author John Gray (*Men Are from Mars, Women Are from Venus*) said it best:

> "If I seek to fulfill my own needs at the expense of my partner, we are sure to experience unhappiness, resentment, and conflict. The secret of forming a successful relationship is for both partners to win."
> — John Gray.[15,36]

Always remember how critically important it is that you do all you can to manage your time wisely. Hopefully, this will provide you and your family with the real quality time you can enjoy and make meaningful.

The Stress of Travelling and Vacation

Taking time out of our busy lives may mean getting away from our residence to sometimes very distant places or sometimes places that are relatively close to our own homes. This means that our mode of transportation will vary according to where we are going. The stress level often associated with doing these supposedly non-stressful or relaxing ventures can be extremely high.

Among the critical factors related to this aspect of stress reduction in part are prevention and preparation. Suppose you are going on a trip or vacation by airplane, national or international. In that case, it is incumbent on you to have at the very minimum your appropriate travel documents. Also, your medical preparedness should include shots/vaccinations where applicable, adequate supplies of medications, and plan for potential medical treatment if necessary. In addition to this having an awareness and knowledge of where you will be staying, security risks, and exit strategy back to home, if necessary, should be part of your plan.

Finance is always a factor. Ensure that you have a realistic cost of your vacation and how you will access or carry your funds, particularly when you are in a foreign country.

Another important thing; your carry-on luggage should contain all that you need to sustain yourself for one to two days at a minimum should you not be able to access the luggage you checked in at the time you get to your destination. In general, do not put anything in your checked baggage that you can not afford to lose.

In most places that you will visit, the people will be kind and good to you. However, let this not blind you to the fact that there is crime everywhere, and you should always be prepared and do everything you can to prevent or reduce the risk of yourself being a victim. In addition, ensure that the communication device you will be using - your cell phone or others is functional and does not cost you a fortune there or when you get back home.

The method of transportation that you choose locally at your vacation destination can be a significant factor determining your vacation's success. Will you be renting a vehicle or utilizing the local transportation services? How much do you know about driving in the country where you are going or their local transportation services? Will you have a tour guide, or do you know friends or family where you are going, and can they help and at what cost? Remember that nothing is free. Sometimes it may be worthwhile, particularly at vacation destination areas that you are unfamiliar with, to consider as part of your vacation a package deal having travel and tour guide during your stay, as well as designated and verifiable reliable places. Doing so, in part, will help reduce your stress level and provide you with a greater level of safety and security than you probably may be able to obtain by yourself. But, of course, this doesn't take away the risks or the need for you to exercise caution while vacationing.

You may sometimes find that you will also have to deal with delays, cancellations of flights, or other transportation services, bad weather, and other unforeseen circumstances that keep you sitting and waiting in airports or transport terminals for an extended time. Or even worse, sometimes being taken to a hotel for an overnight stay. These are sometimes very difficult to deal with, but when you are even partially prepared and accept this as part of the reality of traveling, your stress level will be at a more tolerable level. There are times when there is no good solution when these things happen, but at the very least, ensure that you have adequate food or snacks, reading materials or books, functional electronic devices such as laptops, tablets, or cell phones ready to go. Or just do whatever you find appropriate to occupy your time without being bothered by situations in which you have very little or no control. Needless to say, direct flights are generally better options in most cases, but of course, these things also happen when you are traveling on them.

Local travel or vacations, particularly in your own country, will require less preparation in general. However, one still has to exercise an appropriate level of caution and preparedness to reduce the stress level that can potentially turn what is supposed to be a relaxing and beautiful time into one of trauma and stress.

Finally, it is critically important that you understand and familiarize yourself with the custom, culture, and laws (specifically regarding immigration) that govern where you are going and plan to live within those boundaries. Ignorance will not serve you well, so be prepared.

Words of Caution or Comments

1. You should always make quality time for the people that are in your lives that are important to you. They will not be around forever. Neither will you.
2. Ensure that you make enough time to get adequate rest, even if it means simply doing absolutely nothing.
3. You may own a treadmill, but you don't have to spend your entire life on it. So get off and enjoy your life with the ones you love.
4. It is critically important that you not present yourself to your family with just what is left of you after everyone else has literally used you up for their own purposes with your consent. Your family should have some of the best of you as well.
5. Reduce the stress level during your personal moments with your loved ones. Pay attention to their needs, get off your electronic device before they destroy it or it destroys your relationship.

CHAPTER 7

Protect Yourself and Your Possessions, and Ask the Right Questions

Protect Yourself and Your Possessions

One of the primary objectives of most human beings is acquiring material possessions, personal things, wealth in various forms, and even in some instances, the unthinkable: owning other human beings. Once these objectives are met, the process is repeated several times to attain the result repeatedly and, in the process, gain more of the same thing.

There is often a lot of stress in acquiring some of these things or possessions. But there is even more stress in protecting what you have acquired. You spend countless hours worrying about losing your acquisitions in one form or another, whether it's because someone or some act such as a disaster takes away some or all of what we have from you or an event results in a substantial loss of your possessions that you considered to be significant. The stress level that comes with trying to hold onto your possessions, securing them, and preventing others from getting or taking them away from you can be extremely overwhelming.

Now, this does not only apply to those who have a lot to lose but applies to just about everyone who has things they consider to be of value, which means something special to them. Sometimes it may not be of apparent monetary value. Still, it may be of some sentimental value or something of a cherished memory with a specific meaning to that person who wants to preserve that object.

The big question becomes, how do we protect ourselves, protect our properties, or our possessions? Of course, if we cannot protect ourselves, then it is less likely that we can protect our possessions. Let us look at some basic scenarios. Just about everyone is familiar with insurance. There are so many different types of insurance: healthcare, disability, home or property, automobile, personal liability, life, specialty for items such as jewelry, paintings, and a host of other things. In addition to the availability of these different insurance, there are subcategories of insurance that provide protection for various things. Clearly, it is crucial to have insurance to cover anything that you may consider significant or has some value. What insurance does in part is potentially provides you with funds to facilitate the replacement of your loss or provide funding for services that reduce your liability for expenditures that you are responsible for. Having the appropriate insurance coverage for essential things in your life is necessary to reduce the level of stress you may face. However, sometimes some people fail to have adequate insurance, have no insurance, or even have too much. Clearly, a balance must be reached.

A major component of insurance or its variant is self-protection. It is vital to protect ourselves and our family members as much as we need to protect our homes or other physical structures. Therefore, the use of an appropriate alarm, camera, or monitoring system, smoke detectors, carbon monoxide detectors, and other such safety devices are often very essential.

You may also choose to have one or several firearms or other weapons safely stored in your home as dictated by your state or country's laws. You may feel very comfortable without the need for weapons and decide that you are safe with prayers, or you may elect to go with both options. Others may use guard dogs, or maybe security, and some of you may live in a reasonably secured or gated community with guards and community patrols. Or you may simply choose to be without any of these things that I have mentioned here. However, individual protection of our family and our possessions is an essential function of our lives, and without that, there is likely to be a higher level of stress. I certainly cannot and will not even attempt to tell you what is appropriate for your family's protection. The country, the states, the region of the world you live in, your own preferences, and the laws and regulations governing your jurisdictions may ultimately determine the choice you have to make in personally protecting yourself and your family.

As we all grow in life and collect material things, we also collect documents and files. There are so many different and important documents that we are responsible for protecting. We can get so stressed about what to do with these things that we often fail to find an appropriate place to put or store them. Fortunately, we are in the computer age. Just about everything that we have in the form of a document can be stored safely and easily and efficiently retrieved when needed. Some people will now store or keep everything on their personal computer and then worry about losing their computer. Or some walk around with a flash drive, which has most of their life story on it, and they will do everything to protect it. There are so many services now that are available that can store documents and provide us easy access to use those documents in real-time. There are many cloud-based storage and services offered by many companies, including Google, Microsoft, Zoolz, pCloud, IBM, Dell, and a host of other companies, that can be helpful. You can also secure your backups on external hard drives that can hold large amounts of data and information. This also allows for frequent updates and gives you the option of reasonably backing up your information or data. Therefore, you have numerous available storage options and many electronic file services, not limited to these; hence, you do not need to worry. At the very least, you should have decreased your level of stress about losing them.

There is no reason why anyone has to carry tons of folders and bags of papers to places to get things done. Those days are behind us. Despite this, many people still travel around with many copies of files or paper folders. No one should now be in a position where they are losing hard copies of important files or documents because they are kept in a folder, suitcase, briefcase, car, or anywhere. All these can now be safely stored electronically using a computer to access them from anywhere. Also, we have the option of making hard copies of these documents that could be kept in a safe place in our home. Or we could keep such documents in a safety deposit box, something that everyone should have. This method is slowly becoming extinct as we become more computerized, and the need for that is becoming less relevant and more obsolete.

As crucial as our computers are to us, whether it's a desktop, tablet, or smartphone, losing them should not be something that we agonize painfully over simply because we have lost any of them. Losing any of these devices should only stress us because of the device's intrinsic value but not because of the data or information stored on the device. We should be pre-emptively storing all our important information in the cloud or using other services that allow us to retrieve our information or data if we should lose any of our devices.

Even though the use of computers has technological benefits that come with them that are so essential to our lives, there are often obstacles that must be faced, which can lead to a lot of stress. These may range from identity theft, breach of our banking or financial information, potential theft of finance, breach of our medical records, and forgery, among other things. Therefore, it is incumbent on us to ensure that unauthorized use or access to our information is protected. There are now options for multiple-step verification to access our electronic information. Although sometimes a little cumbersome, using these systems can really prevent or reduce the risks of an unauthorized breach of our electronic accounts. It is essential to utilize these options as they will ultimately reduce your level of stress and frustration should your accounts at any level be breached. These include your social media accounts as well as other relevant electronic accounts that are important to you.

Another critical factor that often is overlooked or taken for granted is the use of emails and the potential risks of accessing them as crucial as they are. Your information can be accessed by opening an email or a link that gives others unauthorized access to your computer data or information without you realizing what is happening. Therefore, it is incumbent upon you to ensure that you are only allowing and opening emails and links that are valid and safe. It should go without saying that you should not give your banking information for a wire transfer or other access to your accounts without thoroughly verifying the party's identity and the account numbers to which you are sending or receiving funds. Neither should you give access to your accounts without being thorough in your verification process regarding the intended recipient's or donor's legitimacy. Often this can be verified by phone call (trusted number) or sometimes a test transfer of a minimum amount (less than $1).

So much of what we do today is **password-dependent**. Although this is becoming less important as we are approaching the implanted human electronic chip era, we still need to ensure that a password is very strong and updated periodically. Strong means that your password should not contain your name, username, phone number, commonly used words, or phrases. You should protect them, and of course, do not share them or write them down, and if it's important, do not save them in your browser. Also, do not use the same password for multiple logins or multiple companies. Make it more challenging to be breached or cracked; use longer passwords, with upper and lowercase letters mixed in with characters (examples: !, >, @,%,$,&,#).

Our smartphone is now our electronic chip that connects us to almost everything we do or are involved in. Therefore, it is crucially important that you protect it like your life depends on it because it just may. Also, it is essential to remember that our electronic devices are always at risk for a breach. Therefore, firewalls, preventing malware, antivirus programs/software, etc., are crucial and indispensable for those who use electronic devices, which happens to be most people. As simple as these programs may appear, they can prevent you from having significant problems in your life.

An excellent example of the need for proper digital safeguards is seen in the management or trading of cryptocurrencies. In addition to the stress caused by investing in them, there is overwhelming stress in protecting them. We are very familiar with going to the bank or calling the credit card company and complain if someone fraudulently steals from our bank accounts or our credit card. This is usually resolved with us getting our funds back. However, with cryptocurrency, when the transaction is completed, it is typically final. That means there is generally no good option to reverse that transaction. There's no one, in general, to complain to, even when you are using a centralized platform.[100] Your odds of recovering any loss are even worse, being just about zero when your operation is decentralized.[99] So, it is essential to ensure that you take all steps to protect your cryptocurrencies. Ensure that you understand and follow the latest technology available to protect your investment against unauthorized breaches of your account. You must utilize appropriate cold or hot storage, using multi-step verification, solid and effective passwords, protecting your electronic devices such as your computer, smartphone, and tablets, and continuously safeguarding your electronic data.

Therefore, taking these pre-emptive steps applicable in the digital world and implementing appropriate protections will ultimately lead to a decreased stress level that you could potentially experience without them. [98]

Another significant action necessary in protecting yourself and your family is ensuring that your assets, however small, are protected. There are many ways to do this. This, of course, will depend on how much assets (the value) you do have and how concerned you are about them, and whether you believe the asset is worth protecting. There are many asset protection attorneys that are available that will advise you on how to protect your assets. In part, the basic process involves having a will or living trust as part of your assets protection. There are significant differences between both that are extremely important. You may also consider forming one or more corporations or obtain an insurance umbrella policy depending on your risks and liabilities. However, as indicated, this is an area that requires additional expertise and understanding of the laws that govern your jurisdictions, the type of assets that you have, and the best ways to protect them. And, do not underestimate yourself or the value of your assets.

The Legal System

The legal system that you have in your country and most parts of the world is not designed with fairness, what is morally right, spiritually correct, or what is generally always considered rational. The law is simply the law and is based on what our government and the leaders of our jurisdictions have set in practice. Understanding this principle will allow all of us to appreciate when the law is not working the way we believe it should. Therefore, when it is time to change the laws to reflect what is fair and just for everyone, there is likely to be greater acceptance. So don't stress yourself or frustrate yourself with what is wrong with the law but instead do what you can to change the laws as they exist wherever you are in the world. Having a legal system that represents all the people that is fair and just will ultimately lead to less stress.

At some point in your life, you are likely to be involved with the legal or justice system regardless of where you live in the world. This may be anything ranging from civil action to criminal actions. You may receive a letter with specific demands from some entity or attorney, a subpoena requesting your presence in court, or for you to testify as a witness in some proceedings or depositions. Or it may be one where it is a demand or warning of some form that requires specific action from you, which will result in adverse consequences if not done. Sometimes you may be involved in a lawsuit where you are either plaintiff or defendant. Whatever the circumstances are, any of these can be a very stressful situation, particularly if you have minimal experience dealing with the justice system as it exists in your part of the world.

If and when these occur, and the feeling of being overwhelmed is at its extreme level, here are a few things that will be helpful:

1. Assume that what is happening is real and valid until proven otherwise.
2. Do not ignore or delay ascertaining what you will be confronted with (open the letter).
3. Understand the timeline that requires action or response from you.
4. Generally, you do not have to stop everything you are doing and attend to this matter right away. Take a deep breath, do not overreact, but rather make a concerted effort to seek advice from those close to you that you trust; of course, legal advice is often necessary in these cases but not always needed.
5. Do not immediately respond by reaching out to those demanding or requesting actions from you unless you have a detailed crafted plan of action that will ameliorate the situation. In addition, you must be reasonably sure of their likely response to you. In most instances, you may have absolutely no answers in the first few days, and that's okay. But whatever you do, do not try to resolve these issues when you have no idea of the consequences or the ramifications of what you may say or do.
6. Remember this, the judges, attorneys, and the people behind this are not much different from you at the end of the day.

However, they may be in a position of authority that can potentially impact your life adversely. So the point is, do not be afraid of the legal system and the people you will have to face to resolve whatever issues you are confronted with.

7. Whatever you do in life: do the best you can to live a morally good life, exercise fairness to others in the things you do, and always take precautions in terms of contracts, agreements, and your affairs that protect you legally. Do the best you can to know and follow the law. Although this will not completely protect you from anything that I discussed, it will give you a better chance of being on the right side of the law, and you will heighten your probability of prevailing in any legal matters. Ignorance is no excuse, and of course, you have no control over who will take you down the path of "seeking justice."

There are some companies that offer legal protection plans. These may provide some limited advantages that may be helpful sometimes in reducing your stress. For example, they might reduce the risk of you being pulled into unnecessary significant litigations. However, there is no protection against lawsuits other than preparing yourself for that possibility should that ever happen to you by doing some of the things contained in this book and others.

Things of Sentimental Value

Things of sentimental value sometimes and often cannot be replaced by insurance or by money. You must take an inventory of everything you have in your possession in your home and your business. Simply determine what are the things that you could afford to lose or simply not stand the thought of losing. These may be photographs of family members from long ago, perhaps a unique painting that you have, maybe a special dress or item of clothing that you have which means something to you and probably only you. There may be other memorabilia that is significant. These are things that you probably want to store in a special safety case, probably fireproof, or you may wish to store at least some of them in a special safety deposit box, depending on the objects that you are trying to preserve.

A good rule of thumb is if you should go away and come back and your home was gone, burned down, or demolished, painful as that might be, the big question should be, what is in your home that you cannot afford to lose? Despite what we may think of in our homes, some of us will have a few irreplaceable things. However, most of the things that are there can be replaced and often with better things than are currently present in our home. The point is, take stock of what you do have, what you cannot afford to lose, and protect them. This action will be a significant contributing factor to stress reduction or worry should the worst happen.

There is a lot at stake in protecting yourself and your possessions. You need to take a detailed inventory essentially of your life and make every effort to ensure that you and your possessions are safe, but more importantly, your families are safe. Former Secretary of State and Chairman of the Joint Chiefs of Staff Colin Powell said the following:

> "Never neglect small details, even to the point of being a pest. Moments of stress, confusion, and fatigue are exactly when mistakes happen. And when everyone else's mind is dulled or distracted, the leaders must be doubly vigilant. Always check 'small things.'" — Colin Powell.[76,77]

Your Stress Level Correlates With Your Finances

The stress level that you have is related or correlated with your finances in most instances. In addition, the success that you and your family will have in life will in part depend on your financial status. Therefore, it is critical to ensure that you take appropriate steps to ensure that your creditworthiness is protected, in addition to having a budget. Make it a habit to know what is in your credit reports. Every year, everyone is entitled to a free credit report from the three major credit bureaus: TransUnion, Equifax, and Experian.[104] It is also essential to know what your credit scores are from these bureaus as well. You may even find it very useful to invest in a credit monitoring service that will provide you with an alert regarding activities occurring on credit reports. This can be extremely critical in reducing the risk of unauthorized use of your personal information and protecting you against identity theft. Prevention is often a better option than trying to resolve a problem after it has manifested.

Two Very Important Questions Everyone Should Ask

What is the worst thing that could happen? Follow up by asking this: **what action can I take now to prevent it from happenin**g? In dealing with stress, we are always confronted with challenges or decisions, and sometimes these are obvious, and sometimes they are more subtle. But answering these two questions is extremely crucial in almost every important decision that one makes. First, it is simply: what is the worst thing that could happen? What if I: go out on a date with this person, marry this person, go on this vacation, go on this business trip, buy this home, let my child sleepover at a friend's house, or agree to pay for repairs of this car? Clearly, the list is endless. Second, the converse of this question is also relevant: what if I did not? These two questions must be evaluated similarly.

The process begins by evaluating each question and obtaining all the relevant information and facts pertaining to the particular action being considered. In addition to answering the first question, obtaining the same information and facts is required for the follow-up question: **what action can I take now to prevent the worst from happening?** Once you have completed your due diligence and the relevant information and facts have been ascertained, it's time to answer the first question by making an informed decision and taking action. However, most of us, sometimes the best of us, never take the time to do this, leading to wrong personal, business, or professional action being taken. Once such action is taken, the potential for a high-stress level will depend on its importance.

Let us look at the following case of Mr. Kim selling one of his properties to Ms. Jones. Mr. Kim's house was worth $600,000; however, Mr. Kim decided to sell the house for $575,000, below market value, for a quick sale and make a $5,000 contribution to Ms. Jones' closing costs. After the inspection report returned, Ms. Jones requested that the swimming pool equipment and heating units be repaired or replaced. Mr. Kim believed the repairs of all those relatively new equipment would cost about $2,000, so he offered to fix it. However, once the repairs started, the equipment cost was closer to $9,500 because some equipment could not be repaired but required replacement. Both parties were in a binding contract; therefore, Mr. Kim suffered a significant loss, much more than he anticipated, as all the parties involved were unwilling to compromise. However, if Mr. Kim had considered the worst-case scenario of the equipment's replacement costs, he would probably not have offered to fix the pool equipment for Ms. Jones.

Therefore, taking the time to consider the worst-case scenario would have prevented this from happening, or at the very least, Mr. Kim would be in a better position if he had exercised due diligence. Making assumptions on significant decisions can be very dangerous. This underscores the need for factual information on which to base one's decisions, particularly in crucial circumstances. Although this case applies to a real estate transaction, it is evidently clear that the same principle will be applicable in most instances to many actions that we take in our lives.

Although stress is likely to be the outcome of scenarios like this, where the wrong actions were made or bad decisions were made, another side is worth considering. This can be very uplifting: one could also consider, **what is the best thing that could happen if I do this?** The follow-up question would be similar: **what action can I take now to make it happen?** Life is a balance, and as we live it, regardless of how crazy it gets or how busy we feel, or whatever action we are taking, let us always remember that it doesn't matter how bad or sad things look or appear. There is always hope. Maya Angelou, among others, once said this:

> "Life is not measured by the number of breaths we take but by the moments that take our breath away." — Maya Angelou.

Protect yourself, your family, and your possessions but always remember to cherish the moments in your life that take your breath away.

Reduce Your Stress of Buying, Selling, Acquiring Goods or Services

This chapter focuses on protecting your possessions, and some of the associated stress are discussed. However, a significant level of stress is almost always present in buying, selling, acquiring goods or services, particularly of considerable value. Some important key factors that can help reduce your stress level are:

1. Do your best to ascertain accurate value or evaluation of the goods or services involved in any critical transaction. Fortunately, there are multiple options available to assess just about any goods or services. You should always use the option of multiple evaluations in significant transactions where possible. Research is a critically important part of the process that allows you to proceed through these actions cautiously with greater clarity that your interests are protected.

   Of course, it is also essential to tailor the level of stress you have according to the value or importance of the goods or services involved. For example, one should not have the same level of stress in purchasing a home as they have for buying its furniture.

2. The next significant element is the people that are involved with facilitating or consummating the transactions. Much of the interrelationship among people have been discussed throughout this book. It is vital in simple terms to: "trust but verify."

3. Understand clearly the terms and conditions under which you can obtain refunds, termination of agreements, and how that process works. If you can pay by secure payment, credit card, or third-party, that may also provide additional protection.

4. Contracts are often involved in most major transactions. If you do not understand them, do not sign until you have

someone who does. This person should be able to help protect your interest, probably an attorney or others.

In the final analysis however, your goal should be to acquire the things that make you happy as well as others. Strive to be fair to others in your business affairs. It will make a positive difference in your stress level.

Words of Caution or Comments

1. If we have anything of value that can be taken or stolen or destroyed, those things should be protected and not left available so that they can easily be taken away from us or be destroyed by others.
2. Successful protection of your family, your life, and your possessions depend in part on these two questions: What is the worst that could happen if you do this, and what can you do now to prevent it?
3. In your pursuits of acquiring possessions or positions in this world, it is essential to remember that true success in part encompasses attaining a status in life where the actions you take and the decisions you make are not determined by how much money you can gain.
4. We all have a value in life, sometimes defined by economics, morality, spirituality, or however we define it. Be mindful of the evaluation you put on yourself. Someone might just be willing to pay your price.

5. The best opportunities come to those of us who are most prepared; we should never stop striving for constant improvement in every aspect of our lives.

SECTION THREE

SOME NECESSARY *MENTAL ACTIONS* YOU NEED TO TAKE TO REDUCE YOUR STRESS LEVEL

CHAPTER 8

Accept Who You Are and Reduce Your Stress Level

When you stand in front of a mirror, do you like what you see? Do you like the person looking back at you? Even better questions are, do you know who you are? Are you happy with the person you have become? Finally, have you accepted yourself, although you may be a work in progress? How do the answers to these questions and more affect the stress levels in your life?

Although we are similar in so many ways, there are so many things that make us as individuals different from each other, sometimes with a unique perspective and unique traits that give us our individuality. Not just with respect to what genetics have given us but rather the impact of our environment and all the various elements it contains. We all have some degree of similar but different backgrounds, different cultures, or cultural exposures or experiences, different traditions, different family values that we were exposed to, and so many things that make us different, or so we think. This uniqueness often helps define us and sets us on a path that some embrace and accept fully or partially or reject entirely. Some of these cultural traits, traditions, and customs, in part, help define who we are, how we respond to life challenges, and ultimately how we classify ourselves. Probably, some of these things that we hold onto dearly or learned were taught to us either directly or indirectly by our parents or our family members. The environment in which we live also plays a significant role as we begin to chart our own course in life. As we go through life's journey, we decide what is appropriate for us or who we allow to teach us, and what we allow our minds to absorb. This process ultimately determines how we think, regardless of whether it happened voluntarily or involuntarily. Now, these experiences often modify how we see the world, how we look at things, how we perceive each other, how we interact with each other, how society as a whole looks at us, and how our impact on society is intertwined.

So, if you are stressed and unhappy because of where you are in life and what you have accomplished to date, that is not uncommon, and although this doesn't help you directly, it is important that you realize that all of us feel that way at some point in our lives. One of the critical factors here is knowing that life is a journey, a marathon journey. Therefore, as long as you are striving for success, trying to accomplish meaningful goals that are probably difficult, then you are more likely to be among the few rather than many who don't try hard enough. So, loving who you are on a particular journey and where you are in life are important parts of surviving and thriving on your journey. It is also worth noting that although we have similar paths and outcomes, we all have different stages of growth, take many and often various detours, live different experiences while ultimately trying to get our own destinations that each of us dreams of. So, love the journey and love the process because you will be spending a lot more time on your journey than you will at the final destination. It is so, so crucial that you do everything possible to enjoy the journey because if you don't, your level of stress might be one of the things that could derail you or at the very least make your journey less pleasurable and more complicated than it needs to be.

The stress we often face in life sometimes comes down to our inability to exercise enough discipline, dedication, and perseverance to see a project, a plan, or goals that we are working on succeeding. Some of us want our goals to be done yesterday, but we are not putting in the work to get it done on a daily basis. Sometimes we procrastinate or simply make excuses for not doing the things that will allow us to accomplish our goals. Some people reach for short-term pleasures and satisfaction rather than enduring less immediate gratifying tasks or objectives that will ultimately lead to more lasting and rewarding long-term benefits. Interestingly enough, when things do not appear to be going anywhere fast, they stress about potential failures even though they have not done enough to create a different successful outcome.

Brian Tracy, a Canadian-American motivational public speaker and self-development author, suggested:

> "Decide upon your major definite purpose in life and then organize all your activities around it." — Brian Tracy.[34,35]

Clearly, there are so many reasons why each of us will feel stress that is directly related to each of us personally. It is also well-established that how we feel about ourselves is often strongly associated with how beautiful or handsome we look or sometimes how well dressed we are. Some people sometimes believe that they are not beautiful. This is because they do not see themselves as attractive and take so many different measures, sometimes extreme, to change how they look or make themselves appear more beautiful. In the process, they are trying to fit a particular image that in their minds is consistent with beauty or attractiveness.

This is different from people taking care of themselves by enhancing their looks, changing their makeup, hairstyle, exercising, or utilizing many different and simple, non-extreme options, such as going to the beauty salon and an array of other things. This is not what I am talking about. What I am talking about is, there are many people who believe that there are one or few definitions of what beauty is, and therefore if they are not within that narrow framework, then they are unattractive and, in some cases, simply ugly. This idea of beauty has created a lot of stress for so many people of different cultures, races, or ethnicities.

It is so important to understand that beauty or attractiveness is not limited to one race, one culture, one group of people, or a particular skin color or shade, or anything in between. But rather, beauty extends across the entire spectrum of the human race. It is a common belief that the way beauty is perceived in society in the past, today, and in the future is based in part primarily on how "we" as a society or segment of it celebrate our cultures, records, documents of our history, and live our lives as one society made up of many. The most critical question here is, who is the "we" that creates the narratives that dictate how beauty is seen? Contributing to this is how much we as a society humanize or dehumanize each group of people regardless of their race, culture, or ethnicity. Therefore, if there is equality, there will be greater acceptance of what is normal or how we define beauty. We have now and in recent years seen many different countries that have representatives who were winners of many international beauty pageants. Now beauty is becoming something that is truly in the eyes of the beholder.

Golda Meir, former Prime Minister of Israel, said the following:

> "Trust yourself. Create the kind of self that you will be happy to live with all your life. Make the most of yourself by fanning the tiny, inner sparks of possibility into flames of achievement." — Golda Meir.[15,44]

There is another side to the way you look or present yourselves and how others perceive you. The way you look or present yourself to others or society can often be among some of the major contributing factors that increase your stress levels or put you on a path where you might find a considerable amount of stress relief. For example, some of you will have different skin colors or shades or be from different races. Or maybe you have several or numerous tattoos depicting what is important to you in words and pictures. In addition, you may have multiple piercings on your body that are considered outside society's norm. You may be short or tall, fat or skinny. In addition, your hair may be short or long; you may be baldheaded, have braided hair or extensions, different atypical colored hair, you may have twisted or locked hair (also called dreadlocks, locs, dreads), or you may simply let your hair grow and just be whatever it is with minimal or no care.

You may have different dressing styles, fashion sense, or wear what is culturally more pleasing to you. Or you may dress in a way that is considered professional or corporate or just fit in with the way most people dress. Your clothing may be too tight, loose, short, or too long.

Some of you will have different ways of communicating. Your mannerisms and your personality will often sometimes dictate how you are perceived professionally or socially.

The people you interact with within society will construct or have their own stereotypes or implicit bias. Now, very often, this is formed even before you are seen. Some of these personal features or actions you can change, and some you cannot. In some instances, characteristics that you may be judged by are things you were born with. Some of you are comfortable with who you are and have decided not to change anything about yourself. Accepting yourself the way you are can be very stress-relieving as you are physically and emotionally aligned with yourself. Therefore, your current status may be ideal for you in some instances, but in others, it is not.

Although you have the right to be yourself and present yourself the way you choose, it is essential to understand that your position or status may not necessarily allow other individuals, corporations, or other entities to welcome you with open arms. Ironically, society at large will look past most of what they would otherwise consider negative stereotypes and will accept some individuals who have special or unique talents or skills required in specific industries such as music, sports, etc. Often there is potentially a significant financial upside to accepting these individuals as they are. Of course, one must distinguish these other significant biases and discrimination such as race, religion, sexual orientation, etc., which sometimes form the underlying basis for rejection. Outside of these, and sometimes including them, people form their opinions according to what appears to be most logical. For example, you are more likely to see people involved in the same thing or activities form a greater bond or association. If you are selling or using drugs, you will have drug dealers that are your friends or associates.

It is logical to think that if you are searching for a place to worship, you do not go to a bar, or if you are trying to find the best place to buy illegal drugs in town, you do not go to the police precinct or station. Similarly, if you are a musician, you will have friends or associates that are involved with music, etc. The point is, it is reasonable sometimes to form opinions of others based on their associations and the way they conduct themselves or present themselves. Of course, there are always exceptions, but often the generalization prevails. Therefore, the way you present yourselves to the world is in part up to those who are your leaders, parents, guardians, friends, and those who care about the ones they are in charge of, teaching and leading them on the right path. This will enhance their chances of being more successful and, also in the process, have less stressful lives.

One of the greatest gifts our creator has endowed us with is being invaluable. Despite that, most of us never accept what we were given. Instead, we take the option to set how valuable we are both to ourselves and society at large based on a narrowly defined framework established consciously or subconsciously by others, who sometimes don't mean us well. But how much are you really worth? This is such an important question which most of you struggle with and is the root of a significant amount of stress that so many people face. If you have low self-worth or low self-esteem or do not consider yourself valuable enough, you will fall for anything. You will accept anything. The moment you realize that you are not just valuable but invaluable, then your view of what is appropriate, how you should be treated, what you will accept or not accept, will be clear to most people and, most importantly, to you. The interesting thing is, most of them will respect that, and if they don't, that is OK too. They do not have to be a part of your life.

It was once said by Oprah Winfrey, an American talk show host, television producer, actress, author, and philanthropist:

> "You teach people how to treat you." — Oprah Winfrey.[39,93]

If you think about that for a minute, you will realize how simple but profound this statement is. The moment we take control of our lives, we will experience a life that will ultimately be less stressful.

Mark Twain, an American writer, humorist, and publisher, famously said:

> "Never allow someone to be your priority while allowing yourself to be their option." — Mark Twain.[15,39]

Often, we believe in doing everything to please someone and creating a tremendous amount of stress on ourselves, while for them, we are an option, and they will not do the same for us. If you are one of those people, stop it. It is as simple as that. You will not believe how much your stress level will be incredibly reduced.

Many people often try to just fit into what is considered the trend, try to have the same things as others, or experience the same level of excitement or thrill. It could be said that they have the "fear of missing out." They do not want to be in a position where they believe that they are not having as much fun as others and therefore want to do whatever it takes to join in regardless of the consequences. This can often lead to so much stress, in part because of your situation. However, your lives have similarities; there are usually many differences in most instances with the people you are trying to keep up with. So, allow yourself to exercise control of not trying to fit in or trying to be like others. Remember that part of being human is our uniqueness, and we do not have to fit in. You don't have to look or dress like others or drive the same type of vehicle, live in the same neighborhood, or go on vacation when they do, or even go on a vacation just to keep up. Don't let yourself be consumed by what others around you are doing while trying to emulate or copy their lifestyle or way of living. Attempting to do that will only consume you and create a much higher stress level than you need to experience.

Focus on what your life is about, focus on your goals, the potential success of the things you could achieve, and how they will make you and your life better. But, unfortunately, some of these things that people fight so hard to achieve, acquire, or enjoy are transient. Their value is short-term and sometimes serves only immediate gratification. Usually, there is nothing there that will empower them or make their lives better in the long run. Robert F. Smith puts it this way:

> "The single most important part of running and winning your own race is recognizing that you are enough and that you are an original." — Robert F. Smith.[67,68]

Words of Caution or Comments

1. Don't be afraid to love yourself even as you love others, and know that you are invaluable even when others don't know that.

2. Do not be afraid to bet on yourself. No one knows you more than you. We all have the power to transform our lives and become what we want to be.
3. When you look in the mirror, and that person looks back at you, love that person. Know that you are striving to become a better you. Live your life to the fullest even when you are alone, and let it be a life that you can be proud of embracing always!
4. The moment you realize that you are not just valuable but invaluable, then your view of what is appropriate, how you should be treated, what you will accept or not accept, will be clear to most people and, most importantly, to you.
5. One of the greatest gifts the creator has given all of us is the ability for each of us to define and endorse ourselves. No one knows you more than you do. Remember that, and never relinquish the power of that gift to others who often do not even know who they are.
6. Make it a habit every day to decrease your stress level by feeding your mind positive affirmation of the good and wonderful things in your life, regardless of what else is happening around you.

CHAPTER 9

Understand and Embrace Your Fears

Do you sometimes feel that anxiety, fear, and stress are attacking you simultaneously and that depression lurks around the corner and is part of the grand scheme just waiting to take over? Well, don't worry, many people are experiencing this in their daily lives. The question is, what do you do? How do you control your life and deal with all these demons that often make your life feel like you are in a living hell?

Anxiety and fear are significant components of stress. One could also say that stress is a significant component of fear and anxiety. Regardless of how you perceive them, there is clearly a significant association among all three, and of course, depression. This book focuses on addressing stress primarily, but the association between fears and stress is extremely important. As such, we have to discuss some aspects of fear related to stress. The basic concept or idea is to realize that fear is a natural part of our lives. Once we can accept that, then embracing it is a significant step toward understanding the relationship between fear and stress. This acceptance will also allow you to better deal with stress as it relates to fears.

There are so many different types of fears. Some of them are: fear of failure, succeeding, not being good enough, missing out on what others are getting, death or dying, living, your past catching up with you, being poor, isolation or loneliness, losing your freedom, and numerous phobias. The stress level that one experiences from any of these scenarios will depend on its relevance to them. Certainly, fear can immobilize you and prevent you from achieving your objectives or attaining goals you have put a limit on. But, on the other hand, fear can also motivate you to accomplish things you probably would not have achieved if you didn't have it. Regardless of how fear affects you, there is undoubtedly a level of stress that comes with it, and just like stress, it can be a positive thing or a negative factor. For example, in writing this book, I could decide not to do it if I fear how successful it will be. What if this book becomes one of the best self-help books of all time? How would I respond to the media, how will I look, how will I feel? Maybe my privacy will change, or what if some of the things I have said here are offensive? I could go on and on and ruminate about what is or what if and probably find some reason not to write it.

The point is, regardless of how we look at future challenges of adversity that we anticipate, sometimes, even most of the time, these things never happen, or if something does happen, it is seldom in the way that we imagined it would be. Yet, we nevertheless get stressed about these things and often make the wrong decision because of the level of fear and stress that we have allowed ourselves to indulge in.

Leslie “Les” Brown, an American motivational speaker and author, spoke about our fears this way:

> "Too many of us are not living our dreams because we are living our fears." — Les Brown.[48,50]

The fear of success and what it brings can be a significant deterrent to many people. Yet, we all have to make that conscious decision to move forward even when the outcome is uncertain, the challenge ahead is unknown, and the consequences of moving forward are yet to be determined. It is this hope and optimism, even in times of uncertainty, that can drive you from a place of fear and stress to heights of success and achievements that you may not even imagine. It will also help us differentiate those who have failed to take action when faced with similar challenges. For some, the level of fear and stress is demotivating and paralyzing, while for others, it’s the driving force they need to succeed.

Steve Harvey, an American comedian, television presenter, actor, author, game show host, and businessman, summed it up this way:

> "If you want to be successful, you have to jump, there's no way around it. If you're safe, you'll never soar." — Steve Harvey.[34,39]

You simply have to face your fears and take risks, even when the outcome is scary and uncertain if you want to be successful.

A significant fear experienced by many that creates a lot of stress is the fear of making decisions. The questions that are often asked are: what if I am wrong, what would other people think about what I did, how would I face those people, how can I go on knowing that I didn't accomplish what I should have? I simply let them down.

The fear of failure, as significant as it is for some people, is a significant hurdle to overcome. In part, everyone wants to succeed. In some people's eyes, the idea of failing weighs more heavily on them than the possibility of success. Therefore, they remain in the status quo by simply doing nothing. Sometimes, they procrastinate, trying to find a reason not to act and not exercise their decision-making ability. They continue to find excuses or opinions from others or something that fits their idea that the best option is to do nothing. Therefore, they go through an extensive process of indecision filled with fear and stress, which becomes a significant determinant in their failure to make decisions. Hence, what they will accomplish in their lives, their influence on their family and others becomes very limited.

Trevor Noah, a South African comedian, television host, and author, had this to say about fears:

> "We spend so much time being afraid of failure, afraid of rejection. But regret is the thing we should fear most." — Trevor Noah.[15,78]

The fear of dying or death weighs heavily on many, particularly those with illnesses that they are struggling with or the more aged. It is natural for one to think of their demise, particularly when they are older and they have significant illnesses that they are facing. The stress that is associated with aging and disease is often tremendous. Many older people have been severely depressed as they struggled with the fear of dying, illness, and the related stress that comes with those issues. A significant number of senior citizens are at the point in their lives where most of their life's accomplishments are behind them. Some of them are no longer motivated about living or about finding things to look forward to doing. These are always difficult times, particularly if they are without significant family members who can be around to show their love and appreciation for all that they have done. It is incumbent on those of us who have elderly family members or relatives to do all we can to give them the support they need as they struggle through stress, fear of loneliness, illness, and death. Also, let us remember that because your elderly family member is in a facility or nursing home, what is generally provided is only physical space. Although those facilities offer some activities and try to find ways to entertain and keep their residents engaged, this is not the same as having their family members part of their lives. They still need to be visited. They still need to have loved ones who call and let them know that there are people who care about them even when they are not in their presence. We can all do a lot to improve the level of fear, anxiety, and stress that the elderly face in these facilities by being an active part of their lives.

The fear of the unknown has caused considerable stress for so many reasons that are often unidentified. Of course, most of them never come through. However, some fears of the unknown can be very critical in our lives. Among them are: what if I have a significant health condition? What if my partner leaves me? What if the airplane that I plan to travel on crashes? What if I get attacked by some hate group? What if I don't go to heaven when I die? The list goes on and on. And so does the level of stress that often is associated with this type of fear.

Concerning one having a significant health condition, many will not seek medical attention because they do not want to deal with a terrible diagnosis. This may be related to, for example, cancer, or heart disease, or the need for surgery. These individuals will struggle with avoiding the possibility of their visit to see their medical provider. This sometimes leads to conflicts and stress between partners because one refuses to see the doctor, sometimes even for simple things such as having a physical examination, a colonoscopy, or a prostate exam. Avoidance of these can create an extreme stress level because of not wanting to face the unknown while they are mentally going through all the potentially harmful different things that could happen due to them having, for example, a cancer diagnosis. But it is essential to know that delaying or failing to take action will not cause the problem to go away. However, quick and decisive action can often result in good outcomes, even when the initial news of the diagnosis presented is unpleasant. This may, therefore, initially create a high level of stress. Still, in the long run, you are likely to be better off with the resolution and overall benefits of a long-term solution to the problem, including reducing stress.

Stress From the Fear of Healthcare Costs

Healthcare or medical cost is one of the most significant factors that often create significant fear and stress, preventing people from seeking medical treatments even when desperately needed.

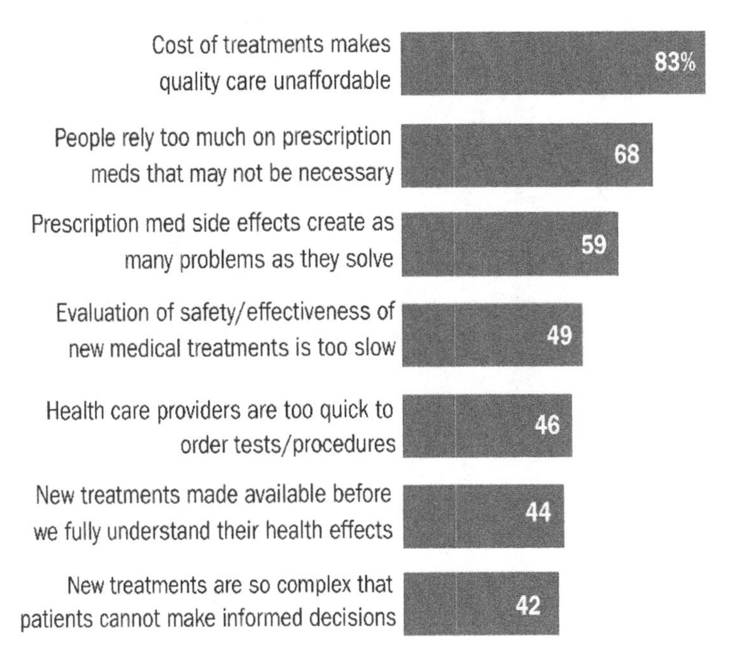

According to the Pew Research Center, 83% of Americans, regardless of their income, believe the cost of quality medical treatment is unaffordable.[106] See the following pie chart:

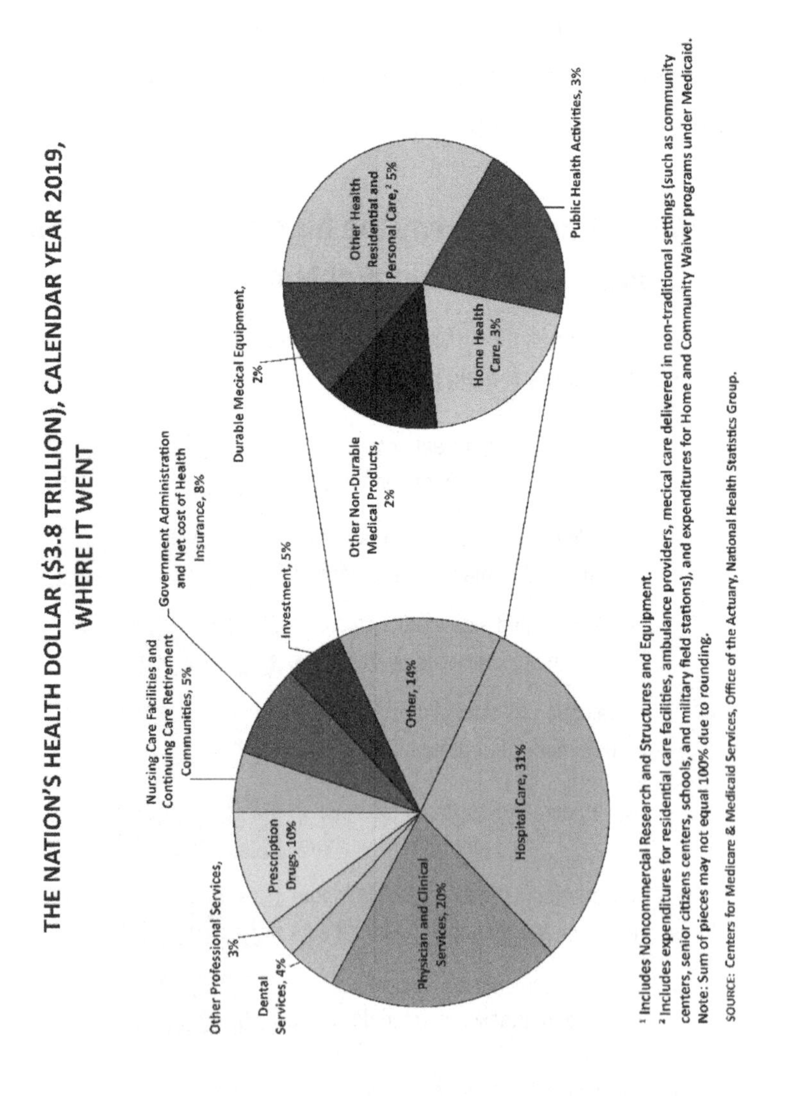

For example, healthcare costs in the United States of America represent about 17.7% of the gross domestic product annually. Or almost 20% of the country's expense. You may be interested in knowing where all this money is going, costing in 2019 an average of $11,582 per person.[107,108]

The United States of America is not the only place where healthcare is a major problem and causes significant stress. Healthcare globally is an essential need and, as such, is of critical importance. However, whatever you do, never allow the cost of healthcare to prevent you from seeking or obtaining medical care, which may, in some instances, be lifesaving. We cannot and should not put a price or value on human life even when it is our own.

After you obtain the needed care in the case of an emergency or before, do not hesitate to negotiate for a price reduction with your healthcare providers and the facilities involved in your care if you had no medical insurance or coverage, or even when you do. In some instances, not only will doctors or other healthcare providers and facilities treat you for free or at significantly reduced cost. You may even be able to find organizations or groups that operate or finance medical facilities that will treat you for free or help facilitate your treatment and payment reduction. Sometimes you just have to ask to obtain these benefits.

So, don't let the fear of the unknown burden you or prevent you from taking actions that might sometimes be lifesaving, sometimes just freeing your mind, or sometimes enabling an excellent opportunity for you to succeed or accomplish things that you may have thought were impossible. All that simply by letting go of the fear of the unknown.

The level of confidence that you have will undoubtedly determine how confidently you face your fear and how much stress you do have.

Marcus Mosiah Garvey Jr. ONH was a Jamaican political activist, publisher, journalist, and entrepreneur who said this about confidence:

> "If you haven't confidence in self, you are twice defeated in the race of life. With confidence, you have won even before you have started." — Marcus Garvey.[15,53]

We must find the courage to understand and embrace our fears. It will make a world of difference in the level of stress we all experience.

Words of Caution or Comments

1. You must understand that fear and stress can drive you and take you to uncomfortable places, but that experience or process often can lead to greater success.
2. Your comfort zone will never change the path you take. Only when you become uncomfortable with your life will your destiny change, even if you are stressed.
3. Sometimes you don't have to **kick the door down** to get in. It is just shut, not locked or reinforced. Just walk in. They may be happy to see you.

CHAPTER 10

Learn How to Express Yourself—Do Not Suffer in Silence

The stress level that we face is sometimes dependent on the words that we hear, or the anticipation of the words that we believe will be spoken or expect will probably be directed at us. This occurs even sometimes when the words are not directly related to us. Words have significant consequences, and our ability to express ourselves can determine the interaction we have with each other as we go through our day-to-day lives. The way words are delivered, in tone, manner, or presentation, are also significant factors in how the recipients of those words respond. What sometimes may cause individual stress is the expectation and fear of how someone might react to them because of what they have said or the consequences resulting from their expression.

A line from *Desiderata* by Max Ehrmann, an American writer and poet, gave us a guide to speak:

> "Speak your truth quietly and clearly; and listen to others, even to the dull and the ignorant; they too have their story. Avoid loud and aggressive persons: they are vexations to the spirit." — Max Ehrmann.[82,83]

Therefore, there is a tendency to hold back from saying what you really want to say, and in some instances, saying nothing. This will only serve to increase the level of stress that is likely to occur because of a failure to express yourself. Additionally, despite your best efforts, there is a reasonable chance that there is an unpleasant consequence of expressing yourself and not having the desired results or response from the person you are directing your conversation towards.

So, one of the things you have to do is learn how to express yourself and not keep things inside while you are literally suffering in silence. You ought to be able to express yourself clearly and assertively without necessarily offending others. However, sometimes it does not matter what you say or how you state your case. There will always be someone who is offended. Often, the truth hurts, and some people just cannot tolerate hearing it. Therefore, they will tend to react very negatively to something that is, in fact, truthful.

Rev. Dr. Martin Luther King Jr. looked at it this way:

> "I came to the conclusion that there is an existential moment in your life when you must decide to speak for yourself; nobody else can speak for you." — Dr. Martin Luther King Jr.[34,39]

It is not always easy to express yourself, but it is something that you have to learn how to do. For example, you have to be able to express your anger or express your disappointment about something that you are not happy with. Letting others know how you feel is essential because they often do not know that something is bothering you unless you tell them and explain; they will not understand. Otherwise, you will be there suffering from the added stress of not being able to express yourself. So, make sure that others know how you are feeling and do not suffer in silence. T.D. Jakes, an American bishop, author, and filmmaker, said this about silence:

> "Silence isn't golden and it surely doesn't mean consent, so start practicing the art of communication." — T.D. Jakes.[37,38]

The challenge of expressing yourself is a significant one in part because sometimes a person trying to express themselves is doing so to someone who may have the power to cause harm to them. Now in as much as you can be advised to speak your truth, quietly and clearly, in addition to being assertive, non-aggressive, or non-offensive, it is not necessarily the easiest thing to accomplish. Even for those who are skilled in communications, an offense is often taken by those spoken to. Notwithstanding, the complaint or the expression of thoughts is considered reasonable by others. This means that you should expect a reaction once you express yourself to others regardless of your best efforts. It may not be one that you want, or it may be overly negative. But it is also essential that you understand that you have no control over the response you will get from the person you are speaking to. You will simply have to brace yourself and prepare for the response. However, despite this, you are probably more likely to do yourself a favor by being able to express yourself rather than living a life of internal turmoil and stress by being afraid to express yourself.

You also have the advantage of knowing that you do not have to say everything you can say. You can make your point briefly, clearly, and while being very measured without offending or attacking the person's character that you are addressing. Now, the question becomes, what if this person's character needs to be attacked? Shouldn't you attack to make your point? While this is debatable, it may not serve you well to attack others personally, particularly if it is your supervisor, or someone in authority over you, or anyone for that matter. So, then the question becomes, if you cannot express yourself completely freely, what difference would it make to your stress level? There is probably no simple answer to that question. However, not every argument needs to be won, and not in every situation where you are right; you have to express that fully. So, there comes a point where a compromise is needed, whether in a business transaction, employment, or sometimes in conversation. You have to allow for some give-and-take. Believe it or not, there will be other times.

Now, what about speaking truth to power? This also has its place. But remember that as important as it may be to do so, sometimes you have to decide whether that is in your best interests or the interests of the people you serve. This may be your family, related to your organization, your business, or professionally, and all those things may come into play. This doesn't mean that you will be silent and not speak to the powerful. Some of the most successful changes in our society were because of the "common people" who refused just to sit back and tolerate what they believed was unjust, and therefore they responded. Each situation will be governed by the condition that leads to it becoming essential or necessary to be addressed. Consequently, it may be best dealt with individually or in a case-by-case situation. Former President Ronald Reagan had this to say:

> "Freedom is the right to question and change the established way of doing things." — President Ronald Reagan.[62,63]

Change can never be brought about by being silent, particularly when it comes to matters of importance.

There are undoubtedly times when people are better served when they have a chance to express themselves, particularly in demonstrations and protests against injustices that have been carried out, for example, against police brutality, racial injustice, in defense of wildlife, or other causes. By demonstrating and protesting, people have a chance to express themselves and reduce the level of stress and discontentment with the authorities or the perpetrators of those that are perceived to be the ones responsible for the injustices. Sometimes, it calls attention to a situation that can be improved if appropriate or reasonable actions are taken. These actions will lead to better community growth and development and reduce stress and discontentment among protesters. However, the people who are being protested against often have an opposite view of the protest, and therefore, they themselves are experiencing some level of stress. To them, James Baldwin, who was an American author, poet, and activist, said:

> "I can't believe what you say, because I see what you do." — James Baldwin.[15,55]

This is the point where it is so important to have reasonable and fair mediators. Whether that be the government or civic groups, who can bring the different parties together and try to find appropriate solutions that will have lasting benefits and prevent or decrease the likelihood of whatever led to the injustice or protests. Change will not come about by being silent; former President Barack Obama said this about change:

> "Change will not come if we wait for some other person or some other time. We are the ones we've been waiting for. We are the change that we seek." — President Barack Obama.[15,44]

Suppressing people's right to protest peacefully while seeking change will not help with stress reduction. On the contrary, it will only worsen in the long run as people try to find other avenues to reduce their frustration and stress caused by the injustice they are fighting against.

The Importance of Proper Communication

Communication between two parties often involves the transfer of information between them. This may take the form of verbal, nonverbal, or visual communication. Now there are times when this is not only crucial, but the communication breakdown can result in significant stress, financial loss, litigations, or other challenging issues. Therefore, the stress resulting from improper or poor communication generally results from the failure to transfer information between parties communicating. The solution in part to miscommunication or misperception is listening attentively and asking the right questions or verifying the speaker's intention with repetition.

Communication is also essential when it is vital to understand what is being discussed, particularly when it comes to contracts. This may be verbal or written. If it is important and carries a significant price tag, it is essential to have it in writing. You do not want to be in a situation where you are misunderstood, or someone misinterprets or misrepresents what you said, or you misinterpret what they said. Prevention is always better than trying to resolve these things later when conflicts develop and there is no agreement.

How good are you at keeping your words? Failure to do so under duress or unfavorable conditions can be very stressful and may even lead to conflict as well as additional stress. If you are going to give your words for something significant, make sure that you can keep your words. If you doubt the possibility of what you are offering, then provide yourself with a fair and genuine way to get out of these situations, whatever they may be. For example, if you said to someone that you would be at a particular place at a specific time, that is pretty straightforward, but if you told that person you would be there at that time depending on when you finish project "A" whatever that project is, or after you discuss it with your partner "Mrs. X," then your words are still valid. Still, it is conditional on any of those factors coming into play. The idea here is having credibility but at the same time having genuine reasons or allowing for the possibility that something could happen that leads to a change, which makes it unlikely for you to keep your word.

Of course, by no means am I saying that everything you do should be in writing or that verbal agreement should not be used for routine things or between trusted friends and those you have a relationship with. However, just be cognizant that there is always the possibility that things could change. If it does, that might negatively affect your relationship with that person, although not always.

The need to have a safeguard will depend on what you are promising or agreeing to do; for example, are you promising to attend someone's barbecue at their home at some time, or are you promising that you are going to take someone to a job interview at a specific time and date? Clearly, there are differences between the two; therefore, your action and level of commitment will vary accordingly.

The way we communicate has the potential to empower ourselves and others. This may allow us to highlight problems or challenges for those that are less fortunate. Sometimes, our voice can make people sad but can make them happy by creating laughter.

Chris Tucker, an American stand-up comedian, actor, and philanthropist, put it this way:

> "I want to keep working, I want to keep doing my humanitarian stuff around the world, shining light on different places that have problems. Keep making movies, make people laugh." – Chris Tucker.[109,110]

The importance of laughter cannot be overemphasized. The therapeutic benefit for stress relief, even if temporary, allows us to connect to a part of us mentally and physically, which only we can reach.

Words of Caution or Comments

1. Being able to express yourself and communicate clearly is critical and will often reduce the level of stress you are likely to experience. Failure to do so can have significant consequences that will adversely affect you for a long time.

2. It is easy to get angry and frustrated when you cannot express yourself freely or you are simply afraid of the consequences of doing so. In these situations, it will sometimes take some tactfulness and restraints to exercise self-control and calmness depending on the reasons to communicate or need to express yourself.

3. Exercise control and of your desire to express yourself and remember you don't have to win every argument, and it is simply not a competition.

4. The words we speak, our voice, is one aspect of communicating. But our body language and tone often can tell a lot more about what we really want to say and what our intentions are more likely to be than the words coming out of our mouths.

Finally, I leave you with this quotation from Nobel Prize winner and physicist Albert Einstein:

> "The world will not be destroyed by those who do evil, but by those who watch them without doing anything." — Albert Einstein.[15,64]

Particularly those who watch in silence!

CHAPTER 11

Allow Yourself to Intentionally Make Decisions

In almost every moment of our lives, there is something to do, or we could choose to do nothing. Every one of us faces choices, some of which are simple and some of which are challenging or complex. It is the mental and sometimes physical activities of trying to process and make decisions that often create tremendous stress as we try to make the right ones, hopefully. None of us is immune to stress associated with decisions because we all have to make them whether we want to or not.

As long as we are alive, we will always make decisions whether we do so intentionally (voluntarily) or involuntarily. Sometimes we let our default mode ("our do-nothing mode") take control and make them for us. Choosing not to make a decision is accepting the consequences of the opposite of not making the decision you rejected, regardless of how you get to that point.

The process of making decisions will vary from person to person. Some people will make every effort to make the right or the best possible decision. They will consider all their options, gather all the facts, seek help where possible, consider the consequences of making those decisions, and make the best possible decision for themselves at that time. They will not allow their default option to take control. Then they make decisions and live with the results. It doesn't mean that the decisions they make will be good or right, but exercising due diligence often leads to better decisions. It is possible that the information they have was faulty, incorrect, misinterpreted, or bad advice from those who had good intentions. This also does not mean that if the decisions were terrible, they should not try again to make other decisions. Very often, when you make a wrong decision, you can learn something from it. You could always improve the chance of making a better decision, even when the circumstances are different.

Now, some will not make any decision for fear of making the wrong decision. They are more stressed about making decisions; therefore, they make very few, or they will search and find all the reasons why they cannot make any. As a result, in their minds, they will not allow themselves to make decisions that could change the outcome of whatever they are grappling with. Invariably, these individuals are more likely to be stressed than those who make decisions more frequently while trying to take all the appropriate steps. It doesn't mean that those who exercise due diligence will not have stress dealing with making decisions. Generally, those who make a concerted effort to control their lives and make decisions tend to have better outcomes and, therefore, less stress. Also, they are not as easily stressed by factors that may easily cause others to be stressed, making fewer decisions than they do.

The critical point here is that regardless of whatever stage you are in your life, making decisions will always be part of it. We will always have decisions to make. Sometimes it will be as simple as what's for dinner, what shoes you will wear to work today, or maybe more complex, like what type of car to buy, which house to buy, or should I marry this person and why? The list is endless. However, the process is very similar. One thing is sure: there will come a time in our lives, sometimes many times, that we will make decisions that are not good and, in some cases, are bad or wrong. Some of these decisions we will be able to recover from easily, and some we will have to find ways to manage the consequences. Therefore, it is vital that we exercise caution in making our decisions but not let that prevent us from making decisions that can empower our lives and others.

Jack Canfield, an American author, motivational speaker, co-author of the *Chicken Soup for the Soul* series with over 500 million copies sold, said this about decisions:

> "Decide what you want. Believe you can have it. Believe you deserve it and believe it's possible for you." — Jack Canfield.[15,39]

Once we have made a decision that is not good, there is always an opportunity to learn from it and make better decisions in the future. Often we may be able to recover from it depending on what is involved. For example, suppose it is a case where you are trying to decide about doing something legal or illegal. In that case, there are consequences for making the wrong decision regardless of how much planning and preparation you put into making your decision. The result of your decision may be catastrophic. It is worth knowing that the possibility of recovering from some decisions is extremely difficult and, at times, impossible. If you base your decision-making on sound principles and core values, chances are you are less likely to hurt yourself and others and abuse or manipulate others. You are also expected to have better outcomes in your decisions. Despite this, it doesn't mean that your choices will be good because you are a good and honorable person.

However, you will see where you made mistakes. You will be able to make corrections for future decisions, which is part of the process. The more decisions you make, the more likely and better you will deal with stress.

Some decisions may result in you being criticized. Sometimes this will be justified, and other times not be deserved. However, this may provide an opportunity for you to learn and improve your decision-making ability. Some of this experience will help you grow. Remember also that as long as you are doing something, even if you're doing the right thing, there will be opportunities for people to criticize you. Some of these will be helpful, and some again will not. But it is as natural to receive criticisms as it is for you to make mistakes. And the key factor here in making mistakes should not deter you from moving forward and making a decision, and doing other things that will ultimately help you achieve the ends you're trying to accomplish.

Robert Kiyosaki, an American businessman and bestselling author of *Rich Dad Poor Dad*, said this:

> "Winners are not afraid of losing. But losers are. Failure is part of the process of success. People who avoid failure also avoid success." — Robert Kiyosaki.[15,35]

It's also essential to know that sometimes when you make these decisions, the only thing you can do is deal with the consequences. As much as we try to predict what others will do in response to what we have done, we have no control over what other people will do or how they will react to what we have done. We must understand that, and when we make decisions, consider that.

When you make decisions, there are always other people involved, particularly if a significant decision is involved. Therefore, it is essential to include the people whose lives may be affected by any decision you make. Hence, give them at least a chance to understand and have the option to be a part of what you are getting them into, to understand the impact your action will have on them by the decisions you make. Often, if people are affected by the decisions they were not a part of, they are sometimes hesitant to join in even though they would agree with what you are doing. This is often because they were not initially involved in the process. So, it is critical to get people on board in whatever you are doing, ensure that they understand thoroughly, and let them be a part of the process of making the decision, particularly when there is a lot at stake. This may be family members, business partner associates, professional relationships, or anyone. Make sure that those people who are likely to be affected are part of the decision-making process. This will save you, your partners, and/or associates a lot of stress and headaches moving forward.

Let us look at the decision made by a doctor and marketing agent:

Dr. Trust and the Advertising Agent, Ms. Chance

Dr. Trust has known and worked with Ms. Chance for over ten years. She has been providing advertising/marketing to his medical practice through a major company that she works for over the years. The common belief was that they had a good relationship that was built on trust and honesty. However, two years had passed, and no business transaction had occurred between the doctor and Ms. Chance.

The doctor wanted to start a new campaign to promote his practice and services by utilizing customized software programs. Dr. Trust initially got estimates from multiple sources and was about to make a decision, but then he remembered the relationship he had with Ms. Chance. He called her up and solicited a quotation from her and her company. She came to the office and discussed the marketing program with mutual understanding between her and the doctor. Dr. Trust also decided to have Ms. Chance's company completely redo two websites he planned to give to another service provider. Ms. Chance's offer was very competitive. Although Dr. Trust usually would have taken some time to discuss this offer with other team members and carefully considered the risks and benefits of moving forward with this project, he decided right on the spot to accept and sign off on Ms. Chance's offer.

Ms. Chance promised to deliver part of the finished product within a few days. Unfortunately, she or her company was unable to provide anything until about three weeks later. Although very large, it turned out that the company provided lots of different services but failed to deliver the required services that Dr. Trust needed. However, by hastily signing an agreement, the doctor ended up locking his medical practice into a long-term contract for products and services inconsistent with the agreed terms. He did not even read the fine print and ended up signing an automatic withdrawal of monthly payments from the company's credit card. This was not even discussed during the meeting. In this particular case, Dr. Trust ended up causing the loss of a significant amount of money without having the necessary service or the expected service that he agreed to obtain.

The point here is, regardless of how well you think you know someone, particularly when you are making significant decisions, always take even more precautions to ensure that you do your due diligence. Also, if this person has been out of your life for a while and then returned, be careful even if you bring them back.

Despite having a good relationship with someone in the past that was trusting and honest, it is essential to remember that people's lives change over time. For example, they may now be working for bonuses, they may have greater financial needs than they had before, and therefore the scruples they had may no longer be there. Consequently, they may not have the same allegiance with you as before or the same willingness to do the right thing concerning you or your affairs. So, whatever you are doing, ensure that you are protected because prevention is always better than trying to solve unresolved things that you should not have been involved in.

Among the many decisions you will make is hiring people to do various jobs. This may range from something as simple as cutting your grass or building a home or something in between, like, for example, installing a hot water heater or having a deck built as an addition to your home. Whatever you do, one of the critical factors in avoiding stress depends on what you understand about the job you are asking someone to perform. If you have no clue or no idea of what you are asking people to do for you, then you are at a significant disadvantage of the outcome of whatever it is that you are trying to accomplish. Of course, this is not always the case because some workers will do an excellent job of what is required, and everything goes well.

However, very often, when people are hiring others to do jobs that they themselves are unfamiliar with the pricing of the job, in which case the cost to them may depend on their sex, their race, whether they appear to be intelligent or not, their age, their neighborhood, the apparent value of their home, or what they suspect the requesting person can afford to pay. Among the best solutions to combat this and often reduce your stress is understanding what you are asking someone to do. Make sure that not only do you understand the scope of work to be done, but you must know and be relatively confident that the person doing the job or assignment understands what is required to be done and how it should be done.

Having no or very little knowledge is a recipe for disaster. The more naïve someone is about the job they are giving other people, the more likely the price for doing the job will be higher. For example, you want to get a hot water heater installed to replace one that is malfunctioning. You are probably saying to yourself, you know nothing about a hot water heater, let alone installation of it, and yes, that may be true. But what's important here is not so much every detail of the process but instead having broad knowledge at the very least so you could have a reasonable conversation with the person that you are hiring.

You can do some research fairly quickly to ascertain some basic facts. There is the Internet, and of course, YouTube. This research could include but is not limited to how much it costs to install, the cost to buy one, how will it be ventilated, what are some of the risks of having one installed, and what is the alternative or are there other options?

Once you start becoming aware of how powerful knowledge is and utilize it, you will find yourself in a much better position to reduce your stress level. Not only will you have a better chance of being treated fairly, but at the very least, you will know when others are trying to take advantage of you or your ignorance. So, make decisions with information that will empower you and protect you from those unscrupulous people in their practice, life, and business.

We have presented some key points so far:

1. In major decisions, always consult with the stakeholders and respect their views and encourage their participation.
2. Read your contracts or your agreement carefully, particularly if there is a lot at stake.
3. It is important to trust others, but people's lives go through changes, so it's even more important to:

> "Trust but verify." — President Ronald Reagan.[94,95]

So, what is holding you back from making decisions? Why do you believe the things you do? The moral principles or core values that you have, who taught you them? Who taught you to love, to hate, to see others as different, and in general to see the world the way you do? Are these thoughts or principles wrong or right?

You see, many people have made decisions that have impacted their lives and sometimes others with significant negative consequences. Some of these decisions or actions can never be changed. The question then becomes, what can you do going forward? There may be others suffering because of what you did or failed to do. Therefore, is it too late for you to stop the pain from being experienced by those you caused suffering?

I cannot tell you what you have done wrong. Neither is this book's objective to make you feel bad about what you did in the past.

If it allows you to make amends for some things that you have done wrong, then that is a reasonable accomplishment that you have attained. It is very likely that you will relieve yourself of a lot of anguish and stress you are going through. It also allows those who you caused or contributed to their pain, suffering, and stress to have some of the same benefits.

Now, there are some things in your life that you have done or decisions that you have made that you cannot change. It doesn't matter how much you would like those things to be different now. Sometimes there is nothing you can do but acknowledge what has happened and find the best way to live with your actions' consequences. For that, I refer you to part of the Serenity Prayer:

> *God grant me the serenity*
> *To accept the things I cannot change;*
> *Courage to change the things I can;*
> *And wisdom to know the difference.*

The question you have to ask yourself is, what are those things that you can change, and what are those that you cannot change? And most importantly, know the difference. It is essential to know the difference and try to live your life accordingly. This has the potential to save you so much stress.

Oprah Winfrey said this about making those decisions:

> "The way through the challenge is to get still and ask yourself, 'What is the next right move?'" — Oprah Winfrey.[15,91]

Finally, in life, whatever you do, whatever decisions you make often lead to other things happening. It is imperative that you understand that the sequence of events that occur in our lives follows our decisions. Therefore, it's necessary and critical that whatever decisions we make, we also think about the long-term consequences and the possibility of what may result from decisions we make now. Very often, the decision we make now cannot be changed. However, we can respond to the consequences or impact of the actions taken by only managing the result from the decisions made. Sometimes, we fail to understand the need for proper timing and sequence. For example, do we buy an expensive luxury car and park it outside of our rental apartment building and then worry about the possibility of it being damaged or stolen? Or do we buy a used car and park it in the garage of our first little home that we have purchased? It is not difficult to see which is more likely to lead to a more productive economic future and possibly less stress.

Words of Caution or Comments

1. Although it's essential to make decisions and sometimes make them quickly and frequently, some decisions are so important that extra time should be taken to process them and ensure that you have done your due diligence and are ready for the consequences of making them.

2. You should do all you can not to make that decision right away. Instead, take some time to step back from it. In other words, sleep on it. It does not matter how good the deal may seem; chances are it will still be there tomorrow.
3. Allow yourself to see things differently and analyze what you are actually getting into. What is it you're committing yourself or your family or your business to? Take time; wait. Unless, of course, you are absolutely sure about what you are getting into and the possible consequences or failure.
4. It is essential to know that the more decisions you make, the better you get at making them. Because even when you make those that don't work out well, you will learn from them and understand the process.

CHAPTER 12

Yes, it is OK to Say No!

The next principle that everyone should always remember in managing stress is: yes, it is OK to say no!

Now, there are so many times people will demand things or actions of you, and yes, you want to comply, yes; it's a good thing, it is a good idea, the person making the request is a wonderful person. But sometimes you must look at your life, your responsibilities, your goals, and you must say no! I am sorry, I cannot do this now. I am not available now. The good part of this process is that, for the most part, you do not even have to give a reason to say no. It is OK to allow yourself to say: I am sorry I cannot help this time. Maybe next time, definitely not this time. Allow yourself the option of saying no and feel good about it.

Saying no is not that difficult to do as long as you have goals and plans in your life and, therefore, things to do. When you have objectives, goals, and deadlines that you want and need to meet, you will find that you are not simply saying no because you don't like the person or do not support their ideas. Indeed, they may have great ideas, great plans that they definitely need help with, and maybe your assistance could be of benefit. However, that should not preclude you from saying no. Sometimes you simply have something that you want to accomplish and just don't have the time it takes to do what they are requesting. Maybe if there is a next time you might be helpful to them. But always be willing and be gracious enough to yourself to say no sometimes. It will reduce the stress level you're experiencing because you do not want to pick up additional tasks or responsibilities that you do not have the time to address. Sometimes you are overburdened by other things that you are having challenges getting done. Know your limits, set your boundaries, say no when necessary, and feel good about doing so. Confucius, a Chinese philosopher, and politician said:

> "Never impose on others what you would not choose for yourself." — Confucius.[72,73]

Now, sometimes this in itself may be stressful. But if you understand why you're saying no and the importance of doing so in the context of your overall objectives in the process of your life, you will be at a more manageable stress level with respect to this process. Also, understand that people do need help, and they have a desire and a need to ask for help. However, this does not mean that you are the only source who can help them. Nor does it mean you have to say yes because you believe they may be offended, or somehow you think that this project or task cannot be done unless you are part of it.

There are so many people who often believe that they are indispensable and their service and input are always needed, only to find out that the job still gets done when they are not around for whatever reason. Most of us, believe it or not, are just an option. Things will get done with or without us regardless of the status we think we may have attained in life.

Saying no means that you did not say yes to something. However, this concept seems very simple when most people say yes. They are looking at the destination, the end result, or the primary goal. For example, if you say yes to your child's sleepover, that process does not just involve sleeping over. It will include interactions with another family or the potential of their neighbors' involvement as well. You are essentially giving up the supervision of your child. You're saying yes to many possibilities, one of which is: your child may be in the presence of someone who you do not know or someone who, if you knew their character, you would not trust to be in the presence of your child, supervised or unsupervised. You are also giving the possibility of your child going on errands with the family or its members. Of course, there are so many other possibilities between the moment your child gets there and bedtime. Everything that that family is involved in, whatever room or area of the home that the kids are playing in or sleeping, becomes part of the process of you saying yes as well.

Another example is that if you were to co-sign for someone applying for a car loan, yes, you are helping that person accomplish their goal. But, of course, you are also taking on the responsibility for all the potential problems resulting from their defaulting on the loan, resulting in the possibility that you are now a responsible party for that loan and all the stress that comes with that. Of course, many of us are familiar with the possible outcomes of lending money to friends and family members

Chris Tucker, an American stand-up comedian, actor, and philanthropist, put it this way:

> "You loan your friend money. You see them again; they don't say nothing 'bout the money. Hi, how you doing'? How's your mama doing? Man, how's my money doing?" – Chris Tucker. [109,110]

Another major factor related to stress is the allocation of your time. Let's say you decided that you want to be a member of your parent-teacher association board. That comes with some responsibilities; however, it might not be very overwhelming. Your commitment may not be as significant as the president of the board, for example. What if you want to run for Congress or state representative or be the chairperson or president of an influential non-profit organization? Then yes, it affects not only your time but also your family members and other members in your circle. Therefore, the effects of all of that have to be considered and not just you saying yes because it appears to fit your goals and aspirations.

Very often, people will make significant unilateral decisions without consulting their partner, resulting in adverse effects. This may involve a relationship of any kind, whether it is business, personal, or social. All these are still affected by the same principle that those people who are involuntary stakeholders have to be involved, particularly in significant decisions. It's not just the process of saying yes and accomplishing the end product result. Saying yes is a process that involves many steps to get to the point of the final destination. When others are not part of the process but are pulled in unknowingly or unwillingly, that will lead to significant stress for them and the person saying yes. Of course, if your partner is going to the supermarket or making minor decisions, that is not likely to be of major consequence that significantly affects others. Then their involvement may not be needed. But suppose they are making decisions that will impact their family or other associates. In that case, those decisions need to be really done in concert and involve those people these decisions are likely to affect.

It still comes back to the fundamental point that a person should know their limits, their responsibilities, their goals, and what they are trying to accomplish. There is no point in taking on responsibilities in which one's performance would be substandard or mediocre. It's imperative that people play their role in life to the best of their ability. Failure to do so will invariably lead to an amplification of stress that will be felt by everyone involved.

Words of Caution or Comments

1. Set limits appropriately and say no to requests that change your life plan or goals. This will immensely reduce your stress level.

2. It is often easy to say no to acquaintances and strangers, but you must have the courage to say no to even those you care about, particularly some of your friends and family members who sometimes have no limits to their demands.
3. Despite the importance of saying no, it is still critical that one does not always give up on the opportunity to say yes when there are benefits and good deeds that could be accomplished by doing so.
4. Saying yes can help someone achieve their goals or allow your family to grow or attain achievements that are only possible by ultimately saying yes.
5. Getting anyone to say yes can sometimes be extremely difficult, but as Tyler Perry, an American actor, director, producer, and screenwriter, said:

> "It doesn't matter if a million people tell you what you can't do, or if ten million tell you no. If you get one yes from God that's all you need." — Tyler Perry.[15,39]

Finally, saying yes to possibilities and yes even to the unknown is in part how we grow and become better than we were yesterday.

CHAPTER 13

Avoid Destructive Behaviors

Avoiding destructive behaviors is an essential part of stress reduction. Destructive behaviors come in all forms, some of which are clearly obvious, and others are more subtle or sometimes even not apparent to those not directly involved. Indeed, there is a range of consequences that a family, an individual, a business partner, or a professional often experiences. In some instances, with appropriate corrective measures, some of these may be addressed, reducing their impact. In contrast, others are so significant and, in some cases, life-changing that the best remedy is only managing the situation as it exists and preventing further deterioration or destruction of those involved.

There are many common ones that most of us are familiar with; the use of illegal drugs is a big one that many people can relate to in terms of its danger and potential significant negative consequences. The repercussions from the use and abuse of illegal drugs are well documented, with impacts ranging from minor acts, psychosocial issues, health-related effects, deaths or murders, extended prison sentences, and a host of other often permanent life-altering outcomes.

Not only are illegal drugs significant factors in destructive behaviors, but prescription drugs also can create significant problems. People getting addicted to opioids and numerous other prescription drugs may experience similar consequences to using illegal drugs. Sometimes, because of the legality of prescription drugs, it can take a while before realizing that those involved in using them illegally do need help. Additionally, the stigma attached to prescription drugs is not always present or applicable to those who use them initially, even when they are doing so illegally. In any event, addiction to any substance often leads to irreparable damage and stress for everyone involved. Therefore, it is not only good for your self-preservation to avoid those drug-related destructive behaviors that create negative consequences in your life, but it is also a tremendous benefit to your family, loved ones, and society at large. Therefore, it is crucial that you avoid these things because your stress level and the negative consequences of those behaviors will be significantly reduced.

The use of excessive alcohol and its abuse, or any compulsive behaviors, is likely to put you, your family, or others at risk. These behaviors are simply unacceptable and add to your stress level and the stress of those you are associated with. Now, there are times when you may be involved in alcohol use; just know that there are limits and boundaries essential to maintain safety. Overindulgence in anything potentially can make even a good thing that is usually harmless transform into a disaster.

Destructive behaviors may also be seen in overeating, not eating appropriately, or literally stopping eating or performing acts to reach specific weight limits (for example, vomiting after you eat) or create a particular image, all of which have negative consequences and come with a significant amount of stress.

There are also destructive behaviors that are common in personal relationships; these may range from domestic violence, sexual abuse, verbal abuse, and child abuse, to name a few. Now, the level of stress involved in these relationships is often extremely high. Besides, these are behaviors that often persist for an extended period, sometimes lasting for years. Thus, the first step of addressing these issues is acknowledging that they do exist. These are indeed very complex issues and resolving each often involves multistep approaches. Part of each of these issues' complexity is that none involves a single, easily identifiable origin or solution. Usually, multiple layers of associated issues or factors are intrinsically part of each type of abuse. Some of these involve many people. Whether they are directly or indirectly involved in the process somehow, knowingly or not, they are contributing parties.

There are also related financial issues that often result in destructive behaviors. These may be seen in personal, business, or employee-employer relationships at different levels or others. By virtue of one person trying to get an edge or an advantage over the other, there are times that can lead to destructive behaviors. How this is resolved or the way it is ratified may be partly the reasons for conflicts and increase the stress level between the parties. There are so many ways that this can happen and does happen. The point is very often, those that have more sometimes become the abuser. How these issues are resolved or mitigated usually depends on the people involved and how much humanity can be realized in these situations.

Now, in a case where it is a personal relationship, for example, between a husband and wife where one may be the breadwinner, and the other is not, one may use their perceived financial power against the other to enhance the perpetrator's desire while creating tremendous stress on the abused.

As we go through life, regardless of our position, or influence, status, or role we play, it is important to realize that whatever we do can and will affect someone else. In some cases, the effects of what we do can be of benefit, and other times they have the potential to create significant difficulty and stress on others. Even though sometimes that is not the intention. Part of our priority could be to make that extra effort to ensure that the actions we take or get involved in do not inflict or cause any unnecessary level of stress on others or create undue burden or pain when the need for that is never warranted.

Another example of destructive behavior is seen in the coronavirus pandemic (COVID-19). The coronavirus has caused the most devastating pandemic globally of our generation. Some countries are affected more than others, and as such, they must take different approaches of how best to manage the virus and all the challenges it poses. Now, there are still a lot of unanswered questions regarding this virus. However, individually, we all have a responsibility to prevent the spread of the virus. It is clearly established that keeping a safe distance of more than six feet from others, avoiding crowds or gatherings, and wearing a mask that covers your nose and mouth are among the things that will significantly reduce the spread of the virus. There are members of some families and others who will do everything to follow these guidelines.

In contrast, other family members will take the position where they do everything else except what will protect their families, their co-workers, or other people. Sometimes just one person chooses to do whatever they want to do, therefore defeating all the other family members' efforts. They will go wherever they want to go regardless of crowds or travel. They simply do not wear a face mask because somehow it is their right not to wear one, and besides, it makes them uncomfortable. They couldn't care less whether they were affecting others. It is a painfully shameful and selfish thing, to say the least. These are clearly destructive behaviors that create significant stress levels for countless families and numerous others in our society, as so many of us are battling trying to stay healthy and alive during the deadliest pandemic of our time.

An essential point about destructive behavior that is so important to understand is that the perpetrators of these behaviors are sometimes unaware of their actions. Other times they are fully aware but continue to indulge in destructive activities. But probably one of the more disturbing things is that there are times when they will be involved in these activities around you, meaning that you are fully aware of what is happening and what is going on. Still, you do nothing to try to stop them or try to make the situation better. Therefore, they continue their activities unabated, in some instances taking your inaction as tacit support of their destructive behavior. And if and when you let this happen, you are directly or indirectly compliant with what they are doing.

Mahatma Gandhi, an Indian lawyer, anti-colonial, and political ethicist, spoke about change in ourselves:

> "If we could change ourselves, the tendencies in the world would also change. As a man changes his own nature, so does the attitude of the world change towards him. We need not wait to see what others do." — Mahatma Gandhi.[15,43]

It's not enough to say you do not care or that it is not your responsibility. As people, we have a responsibility to ensure that we are our brother's keeper. We have a moral obligation to make sure that things are right for each other, particularly those who may not be able to stand and defend themselves in times of crisis and stress.

There are also times when the perpetrators of these acts keep going to the point where they are no longer in control of their actions. This may often be the point when they need medical attention or need an intervention that will take them on a path where there is potential for resolution for them and the people they are affecting. Some of you may wait too long before you say or do anything. Some of you don't want to get involved because it "doesn't concern you" or does not affect you. Unfortunately, this will only mean something to you when it affects you or the people you care about. A better way is to allow yourself to reach out. Be a part of what is happening, not just to your friends or family or your immediate circle of people, but let caring extend to others, particularly when they need others most. We all can make a difference, however small, in the lives of others, by being involved in something that could possibly change the course of their lives, hence removing them from the path of destructive behaviors and adversities and improving the level of stress they are facing.

We have also seen destructive behaviors towards different cultures and various parts of the world in so many ways. Sometimes it is the difference in political ideology, race, religion, sexuality, sex (or gender), discrimination, homophobia, xenophobia, and an endless list of prejudices and discriminations. There is so much stress and often destruction related to these actions. Worse, many people are dying and have died or are severely physically and mentally affected by negative behaviors perpetrated on those who happen to be victimized. Some of this is perpetrated by citizens or people of different countries, different tribes, and of course, by governments and political leaders of different countries.

The toll on society as a whole is immeasurable and sometimes continues for decades after the attack and invasions are long over and done. I will leave you with two quotations, one from former President George W. Bush and the other from Anwar Sadat, former president of Egypt.

> "Murdering the innocent to advance an ideology is wrong every time everywhere." — George W. Bush.[74,75]

> "If you don't have the capacity to change yourself and your own attitudes, then nothing around you can be changed." — Anwar Sadat.[45,46]

Words of Caution or Comments

1. You are not only responsible for your life and the actions you take but also for the impact it has on others.
2. As a society, each of us should not only think about protecting ourselves and our families but also protecting others, particularly those who may not be able to protect themselves.
3. We have control of our mind and what we allow it to do; therefore, we all have control of our behaviors.
4. Professional help for those that are out of control and seem unreachable should be obtained. However, don't wait until things are really out of control before getting help for those problematic people.

CHAPTER 14

Lose Your Toxic Relationships

Getting rid of toxic relationships may be one of the most challenging things to do; so many of us are in very unhealthy relationships. These are relationships that expand the entire spectrum. Some of you will go to great lengths to protect and save each relationship you are involved with. The questions then are each and every relationship worth saving, and how do we know which ones we should keep? For some people, this will be a relatively simple and straightforward process, while for others, it is more of a traumatic event that can be very painful and often cause tremendous stress. However, if we are going to change our lives and reduce stress, this is a necessary process that we cannot ignore and must go through.

One of the first things we have to do is find out which of our relationships are toxic or create an unacceptable atmosphere for us to live and thrive. You then have to take the steps necessary to lose your toxic relationships. Some of you already know which of your relationships are not working and are not suitable for you. Some of these are dependent relationships; others are manipulative relationships. Some of them are relationships where people are in your circles or your presence because they need something from you, but they contribute nothing to your development, nothing to your growth, and you may contribute nothing to theirs. You will find that some of them are more takers than givers. The best relationships are interdependent in life, not one where you give to others and get nothing back, nor one where you take from people and give nothing back. This does not necessarily apply to material things in the strictest sense. Sometimes people get stuck on material things, but there is also an emotional component to this, which is sometimes far more critical than the material things. So, if you are in a relationship like this, get out. Once you do, you will find that your stress level will improve significantly.

Some relationships may be abusive. There are many different types: domestic abuse, sexual abuse, financial abuse, verbal abuse, mental abuse, etc. Some of these are also destructive behavior-related and are covered in Chapter 13. It is essential to get out of these relationships as they will only worsen and significantly increase your stress level. Famous author and poet Maya Angelou put it this way:

> "When someone shows you who they are, believe them the first time." — Maya Angelou.[15,92]

Now in terms of getting out of those relationships, you will find that yes, you lose someone you call a "friend or whatever," but it's

OK to let go of some of these relationships, as brutal as this may be or seems.

Some of you may think that terminating a relationship will result in you not being liked. Or you may have such great compassion for the person involved in the relationship that you are severing it is extra hard for you to do. However, sometimes you have to step back and take a moment to think about what is essential for your mental survival. Also, what do you need to do in order for your life to be in a better state where the level of stress that you are experiencing now will be significantly reduced, as well as all the other negative factors be eliminated or made better?

You also have to know that it is OK if everyone doesn't like you in this world. Everyone does not have to like you. If everyone likes you, there is likely something that is wrong with you, which means that you are probably a pretty messed up person. At the very least, you are probably living an inconsistent life lacking in core values or moral fortitude. If your situation in life is such that you feel that everyone likes you in your life, then it means that you're doing something that is wrong. That is the reality of life. Everyone should not and could not possibly like you. Because we are all so different, when we look at life, it is a bell curve, and there are people at both ends of the spectrum.

In many cases, we all have opposing ideas and principles in life that are diametrically opposite to each other, sometimes at every level. Once you stand for something, if you believe in something, you will be different from the people on the opposite ends of the spectrum of the bell curve. So, it is OK for you to lose friends and sometimes people you believe are close to you. Don't worry about it. It is a normal way of life. So, don't stress about it.

Everyone knows this very basic thought: Jesus Christ was crucified, and there were people who were cheering. Some just stood by, just watching, and did nothing. Probably because they didn't care or may have just felt powerless. So, having people who do not like you because of whatever reason, is OK. In this life, as long as you have within you some core principles and core values that are important to you, that is more important than the people who may choose not to like you. If you have some principles by which you live, you will be happier because you are not trying to please people you will never be able to satisfy, even by compromising your core values.

Former British Prime Minister Margaret Thatcher put it this way:

> "Disciplining yourself to do what you know is right and important, although difficult, is the high road to pride, self-esteem, and personal satisfaction." — Margaret Thatcher.[34,58]

It's important to know that even with your best efforts of trying to find the best relationships to be part of your life, sometimes it just does not work. Some of these relationships are controlling, manipulative, or sometimes there are compatibility or personality issues. Try as you may, you will not be able to change a person from who they actually are. People often do not change much. Their circumstances or situation changes, and they try to adapt to fit them.

Some of you try to apply logical thoughts and expectations to irrational people in your lives, and you are then surprised when they act illogically. It is about time that you stop accepting people's crap and act like it does not smell.

Some relationships fail because people genuinely do not like you. But, regardless of that, sometimes they have to interact, work with you, and associate with you at some level. But don't be surprised if they disappear from your life. That is OK too. In fact, a lot of them never liked you anyway; maybe you are black, not black enough, you are white, you are brown, Chinese, Indian, Jews, Muslim, Hispanic, Asian, mixed—or you are from a foreign country living in their country, or you name it, the list is endless. So, don't worry or stress about people liking you.

There is a crucial point to remember. You don't have to like someone to do business or engage in a professional relationship with them. However, it does help if there is a mutual liking between the parties involved; even more important is mutual respect. This will ultimately make whatever transactions or agreements you are working on be less stressful and more pleasant for all involved.

It's always important to choose our battles without compromising our principles or core values. And of course, we cannot and should not fight every battle, and in many cases, "winning" may not be in our best interest all the time.

Nelson Mandela, the South African anti-apartheid political leader and former President of South Africa, said this about hate, one of the most destructive negative emotions:

> "No one is born hating another person because of the color of his skin, or his background, or his religion. People must learn to hate, and if they can learn to hate, they can be taught to love, for love comes more naturally to the human heart than its opposite." — Nelson Mandela.[15,42]

Relationships are stressful in a lot of ways. One way to reduce the level of stress in relationships is to ensure that the parties involved, when possible, are on the same page in terms of their goals and objectives and how they should be accomplished. Very often, the relationship exists where each person is going in their own different diametrically opposite direction. This is important, even if it is to a limited extent, because it will still have a considerable amount of stress on the relationship, which ultimately leads to conflicts and discontentment. Therefore, it is essential to work in unison on all relationship-related issues to minimize stress at every level. If this is not happening, your stress level will be significantly higher, and the chance of your relationship surviving or being productive decreases considerably.

Have the Courage to Accept it When You are Dumped

This chapter, for the most part, is about you letting go of your toxic relationships. But how about when you are the toxic one, or maybe you are just boring, or here is a big one that may hurt the most: how about when you and everyone else consider you to be "perfect."

Sometimes, even the person dumping you knows it and probably lets you know – "you are too good for me" or "I am not good enough for you," and then simply goes ahead anyway and dumps you! Or by someone's judgment, for whatever reason, you are not who they thought you were, and it's time to let you go.

The level of stress associated with being dumped can be just as significant for both partners in most instances as when you are the one letting go of others. These relationships also span personal, business, professional or social relationships, and their impact often generates similar negative emotions, sometimes even having deadly consequences.

One of the critical factors in dealing with the termination of these relationships is having the courage to accept the rights of others to depart from your life regardless of their reasons or lack thereof. Some of these reasons may be completely irrational to you. However, to them, it makes all the sense in the world, and that's more important than what you think or the opinion you may have of their decisions. Once you can accept that you are in part on your way to recovery from whatever negative emotions you may have due to them letting you go.

Letting go of others who have moved on from you will allow you to create a more positive environment for new people to come into your life. Without letting go of those who said goodbye to you, you prevent yourself from embracing changes coming into your life that could potentially allow you to grow sometimes even more than you would if those persons were still in your life.

Of course, it is not always easy. Sometimes, you will ruminate about all the things you have done and the contributions and sacrifices you made to advance their lives and now feel like you are losing everything. You may be saying to yourself; you don't want to start over. This may be true in part, but the reality of life is that sometimes we lose, win, or maybe we draw. Regardless, you have to find the will to carry on without feeling the need to be punitive or to carry negative emotions for those that have gone.

Harboring those emotions about others will only destroy you and make it literally impossible for you to take the next step, becoming a more productive you. We have seen so many times when people have given up on life, do not wish to go on, or often wish the same for the other person, leading to destructive and sometimes deadly consequences. After being dumped and your level of stress increases, you could find consolation by talking to trusted friends or getting professional help, but whatever you do, allow yourself to let go and move on. Your stress level will be rewarded for the courage you have in doing so.

Abstract Kidnapping Disorder (AKD)

There is an important concept, a medical disorder not previously discussed, published, or classified related to broken relationships. This disorder is what I call "Abstract Kidnapping Disorder - AKD."[114] You will not find this in the medical or general literature. Still, I believe it is likely to be there in the future, including in The

Diagnostic and Statistical Manual of Mental Disorders, the textbook published by the American Psychiatric Association currently in its *5th Edition* (DSM-5).

Briefly, individuals with this disorder have mentally kidnapped the person they were in a relationship with, although they have no current physical contact with them and are unlikely to have future ones. Signs and symptoms of AKD may begin before there is a complete termination of the relationship in question. In addition, they demonstrate features similar to that of the grieving stages: denial, anger, bargaining, depression, acceptance, and others in no particular order. However, in this case, the subject is alive. These individuals will also have both positive and negative emotions associated with their exes. There is an associated increased domestic or other violence levels, often resulting in severe injuries or fatalities -murder/suicide.

The disorder has both acute and chronic stages. The triggers for AKD may include but are not limited to physical and mental attachments that they shared with their exes and elements of newly formed relationships of their exes. Ironically, in severe cases, these individuals may go to extreme measures to find or locate their exes, for example, stalking, harassing, attempting unsolicited communications, etc., which often exacerbates the disorder. AKD is not only limited to personal relationships but also includes business or professional.

Treatment for AKD: therapies that are likely to be helpful include psychotherapy, biofeedback, or hypnosis. In addition, it will require treating any underlying psychiatric conditions, if present:

such as anxiety or depression, as well as treating other nonpsychiatric comorbidities. More details for AKD will be covered in another publication.

I included this potential diagnosis of AKD, which, if present, will be made worse by stress. In addition, letting go of others when they no longer need you because you have served their purpose still remains the right thing to do, even if it takes all the courage you have.

I will leave you with one quotation from Albert Einstein, Nobel Prize theoretical physicist:

> "If you want to live a happy life, tie it to a goal, not to people or objects." — Albert Einstein.[39,51]

However, we must find ways to work with others to accomplish our goals regardless of how difficult it may be, even if that means letting them go.

Words of Caution or Comments

1. The most important people in our lives are not those who are gone or those we hope to come into our lives, but those physically present and connected to us mentally or emotionally. They should be our priority, and we should treat them that way. If they are not, then we should make every effort to get them out of our lives.

2. Get out of toxic relationships and reduce your stress. And when you finally get out of these unhealthy relationships, remember where you are coming from, and do your best not to get back into another toxic relationship.
3. If you are at a point in your life when you could say your relationship is not good for you, it is not suitable for your mental health; it is too stressful. Then, it's time for you to say, OK, this is not working, and it is time to move on.
4. When a relationship is failing, and you have made significant changes to make it better, but everything remains the same, it is time for you to say it is over; I am not who I used to be anymore!
5. One of the great equalizers of broken relationships, disappointments, and the act of moving forward is the fact that we can all rest assured that there is one thing for certain: we always take ourselves wherever we go.
6. When someone decides that they do not wish to be part of your life anymore, it is time for you to embrace the changes that are possible, but only if you are willing to let go of a life that is not yours.

CHAPTER 15

Be Gracious—Give Thanks for Everything

The fact that stress can affect us in so many ways is not surprising in that there are also many other ways stress can be relieved or at least be improved. And what makes it even more interesting is that many of these things that can reduce the stress level that we face are actually free. Another great stress buster is gratitude, just the ability to be in a position to say thank you. We don't have to look very far; just consider the idea that we could enjoy the environment and its numerous elements—enjoy the wind, the rain, all the different colors of the vegetation that we see. Or the sea, rivers, natural waterfalls.

There are so many things that are just nature's way of reaching out to us for which we can be thankful. And what is also incredible is that we can see some of these things: enjoy the fragrance, hear the sounds of birds or all the different life-forms that are part of our world that make living much more fun and wonderful. Amazingly, most of us go through life on a treadmill. We do not take the time to appreciate that these things are there for us to enjoy. They are part of our existence and are among the reasons to give thanks. If we want to be more in tune with nature's sounds, we can do that; there is so much to be discovered and to be grateful for. Those of us who choose to appreciate and love our environment will enjoy a life that certainly has more tranquility and peace. Those who fail to are missing the opportunity to reduce their stress.

Former President Barack Obama understands the importance and the need to protect our environment, as he said:

> "This is the moment we must come together to save this planet. Let us resolve that we will not leave our children a world where the oceans rise and famine spreads and terrible storms devastate our lands." — President Barack Obama.[47,48]

We can always find things to be sad about, things that are not going well or could be better. But if we just take the time to appreciate how much most of us have, we will realize that we are indeed fortunate and have a lot to be thankful for. I have often heard it said that if you have life, that's a reason to be grateful. If you can work or are in relatively good health, you can literally choose anything that is part of your life for which you can be thankful. Many would be happy to change places with you and be gracious for what you are not acknowledging in your life. So be grateful.

An important aspect of gratitude is giving; when you give, there is a feeling of gratitude that you will receive, which does not come from the person that gets the gift. Even though they may be gracious, this is the feeling of gratitude the giver experiences by being fortunate enough to be able to give that gift. So, in addition to giving, allow yourself to accept gifts from others, however humble their gifts may be. Because by doing so, you also allow those who give to you to receive that feeling of gratitude that you receive when you give, even if you do not appreciate the gift they give you.

Have you ever wondered why some people who are givers, however small or large, or those involving charitable works, why they keep giving and working and giving of their time, their money, their talent, or their energy? It is because they don't necessarily need your or anyone's gratitude to be fulfilled. Instead, they are able to benefit from the act of giving. So give freely, and when you receive, even though the giver does not need your acknowledgment of their gratitude, be gracious anyway.

I will share with you an act of gratitude. Mr. Joe is a patient we have been treating for many years. He came to our office and was seen by my physician assistant. It was Christmas time, and he brought a gift for me. Once the visit was over with my assistant, he asked to see me. I went into the exam room, and he presented me with the gift. He explained how much he appreciated our treatment and service in our office, and he wanted us to know that, so this was a way of saying thank you to us. I accepted it and expressed my appreciation very clearly, and let him know that we appreciated him too. This wasn't the first time patients had brought gifts to our office. Many have included food (which we discourage them from bringing) or many different things.

I looked at Mr. Joe's gift for me. It contained two shirts and a pack of undershirts. I was happy and very touched by his gestures of kindness. I walked around the office and showed it to just about all the staff members. I wanted to share it, but there was not much to share because of the gift type. There are two main things that were very noticeable to me. First, Mr. Joe was very happy to have given me the gift, and I was delighted to receive the gift. The second thing is that Mr. Joe is someone of modest means, or probably does not have much based on everything we know about him over the years. However, he made the sacrifice, and it made both of our days very happy and as well as the members of our staff. I share the story just to say that sometimes accepting gifts from others, however humble it may be, can indeed be a wonderful thing for everyone involved. I will definitely be giving a copy of this book to Mr. Joe. I am sure he will figure out that I am talking about him even though I have changed his name.

Zig Ziglar was an American author, salesman, and motivational speaker who summarized gratitude this way:

> "Gratitude is the healthiest of all human emotions. The more you express gratitude for what you have, the more likely you will have even more to express gratitude for." — Zig Ziglar.[87,88]

A sure way to reduce the stress level that anyone is having is simply to take stock of many of the things we can be grateful for. Sometimes we get so busy and focus so much on the things that are pulling us down, draining our energy, or just making us sad. If we only allow ourselves to see all the good things in our lives despite the challenges that we face, we will realize that there is much to be grateful for, and we should.

Words of Caution or Comments

1. Never stop being grateful. It is one of the most significant stress-relieving acts that anyone can utilize free and reap all its benefits.
2. Through our lives' ups and downs, gratitude will always provide us with the desire to persevere even in our darkest moments.
3. The act of giving provides a gift of the joy of gratitude not only to those who receive the gift but also to those that are the givers.

SECTION FOUR

SOME NECESSARY *COMMUNITY ACTIONS* YOU NEED TO TAKE TO REDUCE YOUR STRESS LEVEL

CHAPTER 16

Find Someone to Share Your Love and Something to Do

Find Someone to Share Your Love

One of the most incredible emotions that we all share as human beings is the ability to love. It is worth so much, yet it is free; at some point, we all believe we have it, but then it's gone. It is everywhere and sometimes is nowhere to be found. We see some holding onto it, while others share it and never seem to have too much to give away. As we go through this journey of life, some of us have an abundance of love while others have so little or none, or at least fail to express any.

We have heard it said that for you to give love, you must have love. You simply cannot give what you don't have. Neither can you share it. Nor are you capable of receiving love if you don't have any;

it will be so much harder for you to appreciate love even when you are surrounded by it.

Having someone to love is one of the greatest stress busters anyone could have. Because when you love and give your love, you are opening yourself to be loved. So many of us have so much love to give, but we never truly love anyone. So, allow yourself to love freely and love others; find someone to love. Share your love with others and let that be part of your positive growth and development. Continue nurturing yourself. Your ability to love and your love experiences will significantly reduce the amount of stress that you have and make a significant difference in your life.

Love can result in endless possibilities. Some of them are lasting relationships, some of which may result in starting a family, lasting friendship, helping to enhance someone's life and allowing them to rekindle their dream and vision, or just giving hope to a new beginning.

We are all capable of loving the elderly, those who are less fortunate, our children of the world, watching out to ensure that they are treated well and that their welfare is protected. Love does not only extend to our family and those we are expected to care about, but we are also capable of loving others, even those we have never met. That is one of the universal aspects of love that allows it to bring us together and enable us to reach out and have empathy and a sense of humanity for others even when they may be considered different from us. When you can love in this way, not only are you helping others alleviate or reduce their stress, but your stress level will also be significantly less because of your willingness to share your love with others.

We are not in this world all by ourselves. There are other life forms that make this world a much better place. It is only natural that we should take time to love our environment and wildlife and preserve and care for our animals. We have seen the benefits of pet therapy and how it can transform many people's lives, creating a more enjoyable and better living environment. The ability to enjoy nature has its therapeutic benefits. Whether you enjoy the abundance of water, the geological wonders of the world, or just the vegetation, there is a lot to love. There are stress-reducing benefits in a therapeutic context that are also significant.

In our society today, many people do not believe in love but instead have a significant fear of loving or being in love. It is not that they are hateful or have hate in themselves. Somehow, they see this differently, and that's OK. However, love sometimes has a way of catching up with some people. Then they will understand. From the words of the prophet Khalil Gibran, a Lebanese-American writer, poet, and visual artist:

> "Life without love is like a tree without blossoms or fruit." — Khalil Gibran.[15,102]

Words of Caution or Comments

1. Some people may say that finding someone to love could cause more stress than if they do not. However, it will be much more beneficial and rewarding if you find love.
2. Do not let your fear prevent you from loving anyone. Give yourself a chance to reduce the stress level that comes with the fear of not loving others.
3. In your darkest hour and your greatest need, love may be the only force that can bring light into your life. Open your life to love and be loved.

Find Something to Do

> "Faith without work is dead." — James 2:14 - 26 NKJV

It's so important that in life, we all have something to do. Ideally, if we all have a job, that would be one scenario that will almost guarantee everyone something to do. Unfortunately, many people are without jobs. Some of them probably will never be employed in the future, and those who are retired after working many years, sometimes at extremely difficult jobs, may also be unemployed. Having a job can be very rewarding and therapeutic in relieving stress; it provides someone the opportunity to do something consistently, provide income, provide a sense of well-being, and contribute productively to society's building and development.

Now, one could cite all the stresses having a job can cause and are causing some people, and in general, this is a real factor and is a contributing cause of stress as well, but there are positive benefits of having a job. In this book, we talked about some of the factors contributing to stress and the benefit of dealing with stress related to employment and other issues. It is clearly established that having a job is essential in relieving stress. There is often a sense of hopelessness, doom, and frustration that can set in without anything to do. Also, the negative economic impact or failure to be useful providers can be really challenging.

The purpose of having a job is universally associated with money or some financial gain or income. However, the concept of doing something, whether that be a job, a hobby, activity, or anything that takes one out of the state of doing nothing, is vital to relieve stress and create a sense of well-being. Of course, the activity level that one is engaged in does not necessarily equate to how one feels or how one responds when one has something to do or participate in. However, just by virtue of doing something, most people create a sense of well-being that is essential in enhancing the way they feel about themselves.

The activities that you get involved in could be a hobby. It may be volunteering; it may be taking on a new task or a new goal that begins with a new idea and opens a new set of experiences compared to where you were before you started. For example, you could decide that you want to start painting, start writing, start learning to play a particular musical instrument, or you may decide that you would like to learn how to cook specialized dishes of different cultural or ethnic origins. The list is endless. The point is there are so many different things that one could find that they like to do, creating an avenue for themselves to be more productive. This is likely to reduce your level of stress, allowing you to have a more productive life.

It doesn't always mean that you have to have a physical job or hobbies you have to pursue. So many people enjoy their lives now by spending time with their children or grandchildren, taking them to different activities, and teaching them so many things that these children probably would not have had the opportunity to learn without having the exposure provided by their grandparents or caregivers. These roles and so many others also fulfill an essential part of relieving stress for so many people. Others may choose to spend their time with their elderly parents and take them to different places on different trips, allowing them to enjoy their lives in different ways, and that is OK too. What I have given here is just a small sample of ideas of what can be done once you are at that point where you may feel that there is not a whole lot you can do. There definitely is, and that is the point that I want you to get from this. And just in case you are thinking of giving up for whatever reason, there is always a way forward.

Former President Bill Clinton put it this way:

> "If you live long enough, you'll make mistakes. But if you learn from them, you'll be a better person. It's how you handle adversity, not how it affects you.
>
> The main thing is never quit, never quit, never quit." — Bill Clinton.[15,34]

Is Your Job Stressing You Out?

It is no secret that having a job is critically important to our survival and, of course, has the potential benefit of reducing the level of stress we face. But how about when your job is the main reason why you are facing stress? What can you do? There are many different scenarios where each type of job will dictate the response you have to reduce stress potentially. Some of the things that one should do or consider in the process of stress reduction or prevention are the following:

1. Evaluate yourself to determine whether you are capable of performing the job you are assigned. For example, do you have the required skill, qualifications, or expertise you are paid for?

2. Do you have the support staff and tools required to do the job? Is it your responsibility to provide those, or are others – supervisors, or your boss' duty to do so?

3. Are you producing quality work or products for which you are paid? Is it acceptable to yourself or those supervising you, if anyone, or to those who are expected to benefit from what you do?

4. Do you respect, like, or at a minimum find the people you're working with acceptable or tolerable? Or is this the worse part of your day, which adds up to 40 or more hours per week?

5. Do you have doubts or question the integrity of the service you provide or what your company provides as a whole? Or do you believe that you are part of an unethical, corrupt entity, that at a minimum, steals from others directly or indirectly?

6. How does your job affect your family? Does it take you away from them, leaving you little quality time? Or does your job continue at home? Does it cause conflict in your personal relationship or other aspects of your life, such as religion, politics, or conflict with your core principles?

7. Do you simply just feel unappreciated, disrespected, used, underpaid, and abused and feel there is no way or good way out? Are you just hanging on because of the benefits, healthcare, retirement, etc.? And maybe retirement is just around the corner.

8. Are you working because you need a paycheck and you feel that you do not have a choice? Or maybe you are just working to compensate others for favors, services, or goods you received from them before?

9. Do you spend so much time stressfully traveling, whether by air or ground transportation, that at the time, you simply hate going to work? However, somehow you tell yourself you have to continue working because that is your best option for now. Which, in some instances, "now" has been going on for months or years.

These are some of the things that often create tremendous stress in almost anyone's life. The challenge is, in part, has always been how to relieve yourself from situations like these while at the same time not getting into another worse one. The first step is to be aware of what you are involved in and then commit to changing your circumstances. This may sometimes involve complete career change. Walking away from something that is supposedly secure to that which is unknown or does not guarantee success is always difficult but sometimes very necessary. However, the most significant life changes require making decisions that demand of you to trust yourself and your ability to accept something different. This is ultimately how you can transform your life and be more productive and less stressed.

Words of Caution or Comments

1. Whatever stage of your life you may be in, never forget that there is always something that you can do.
2. Do not allow yourself to be bored or too tired. Never give up on life because negative thoughts will creep into your mind when you are in that state. So make every effort to find something to do.
3. Finding something to do is one of those human traits that every person has and needs to harness to be a productive member of our society, regardless of how humble your vocation may be.
4. Whatever you end up doing in life at whatever stage, always give it your best and strive for excellence. Never perfection.

Pursuing perfection will only cause more stress to you without its accomplishment

CHAPTER 17

Find Something to Hope for

Finding something to hope for is truly another of the great humanistic traits we all have because there is no meaningful future without it. One of the most disheartening things to see is someone who has no hope, dreams, or aspirations and has no vision. It is sad when one feels that their life is of no value or that their life is over, and therefore there is nothing to live for or nothing to gain from living.

Each of us needs something or a reason to get us out of bed each day. It is so important to have hope, or to have aspirations, or to have dreams. These are some of the things that motivate us to want to get out of bed, making us want to do something and be productive. To say yes, I have got to get moving. Yes, I have got to do something for whatever that reason or factor is. One must find hope because that will make a difference to stress levels. The moment when anyone loses the ability to have hope or dream, they have essentially lost the ability to live happily, which will only add more stress to their lives.

So, it is essential for all of us to always think about what is the next thing that we are going to do, whether we are retired or whatever we are doing in life. There is still something that you could do or something to look forward to. For whatever reason, if you don't have anything, there is an essential need to create dreams.

Now, it doesn't matter whether you have a job or you don't have a job. People with or without jobs sometimes have no desires and dreams because they feel they have nothing worthwhile to do. Sometimes they see their future or primary goal among one of these: no plan for the future, I am just waiting until I retire, I am just waiting until I die, or whatever it is. If you find yourself in any of these situations, you have to find a way to get out of it and move on a more positive self-directed path. Not only will this tremendously help your stress level in general, but you will also be invigorated the moment you start looking beyond where you are and toward where you want to go. The burning desire to be a part of something, look forward to being involved in something, contribute to the development of one's life or an idea, the process, or the movement of something that often is bigger than yourself, can be very gratifying. Being a part of actions like these can turn so many people's lives around and allow them to get up and move and do things that are outside of themselves or even outside of their comfort zone.

The sad thing is that most people don't realize how much they can contribute or how much their participation can make a difference. Therefore, they are not motivated to do anything other than what they are accustomed to doing. That in itself is limiting their ability to take their lives in a more positive direction. The process of taking self-directive motivated actions could ultimately lead to a more productive, less stressful, and more enjoyable life.

Sometimes it may be going to a place to volunteer to make a difference in someone's life, but whatever you do, don't just sit there, doing nothing, believing or accepting the idea that your life is over and there's nothing more left but waiting to die.

Dr. Martin Luther King Jr. reminded us that we all have the capacity to serve:

> Everybody can be great because anybody can serve. You don't have to have a college degree to serve. You don't have to make your subject and verb agree to serve. You only need a heart full of grace. A soul generated by love." — Dr. Martin Luther King Jr.[15,41]

There is always the opportunity to do something or create the reality you need.

Words of Caution or Comments

1. Always try to find something to hope for or believe in, and in the process, you will often find something to do.
2. Finding something to hope for will create a dream and aspiration for you that will take you on a path that ultimately makes your life more meaningful and so much more desirable to be enjoyed to its fullest.

CHAPTER 18

Take Some Time Out of Your Life to Help Others

Whenever you are going through a stressful phase in your life, it is often very difficult for you to stop and think of others, particularly when you feel so overwhelmed by all the challenges of dealing with many of the issues confronting you. These are indeed the times that it appears most challenging to stop and help others. However, some people may not know that even during the difficulties they are experiencing, they still have the power to help others. Making an effort to reach out to others who may be in some way less fortunate than you, or maybe going through struggles that are similar to yours, is without a doubt one of the most rewarding things that you could do for yourself. But the amazing thing is that while you are also helping others deal with some of their issues, their stress level will improve significantly. You will also find that even for a brief moment and more, the level of stress you are experiencing will improve even though your overall problems or challenges may remain the same. In part, this does energize you and elevates your energy to be better able to take control of the process of improving stress in your life.

So take some time out of your life to help others. Now, this may be in the form of some charitable work, or it could be simply a kind word expressed to someone or a kind deed or gift.

Mother Teresa (Saint Teresa of Calcutta), an Albanian-Indian Roman Catholic nun and missionary, understood the value of kind words:

> "Kind words can be short and easy to speak, but their echoes are truly endless." — Mother Teresa.[15,52]

The big picture here is that you don't have to give others a lot to make a difference in their lives. Sometimes all it takes is just your kindness, your smiles, or your thoughts expressed to them to show your appreciation. Simple words that are genuinely spoken like: thank you, please, I appreciate you, and others can make a big difference in someone's life or day. It may help relieve any tension present, create a much better atmosphere, and make the day go by better for you and others.

An essential element in this process is that the greatest gift we could give ourselves is expecting nothing back when we do these things. Do not expect a thank you, do not expect a present, do not expect, oh, look what this person gave me; none of that is important. Because when you do these things, invariably, you will be surprised that it comes back to you in some way or another. Not from that person you did help or those you did good for but from others. The strange thing is, you will receive so much from others who have no specific reason to help you or do something that benefits you in ways that you can't even imagine and for which you simply do not deserve because, in reality, you have done nothing for them. You benefit from getting more than you deserve because somewhere, or sometimes in your life, you did something for others, and now it is coming back to you.

Princess Diana, once Princess of Wales, a member of the British royal family, had a clear understanding of the process of giving. Maybe, in part, that's the reason why so many of us loved her:

> "Carry out a random act of kindness, with no expectation of reward, safe in the knowledge that one day someone might do the same for you." — Princess Diana.[56,57]

So, give your time, talents, money, and energy freely because it is so essential and can make such a big difference in so many other people's lives by you giving.

And when you give, share the joy. Some of you may say when you look at yourselves, "I am poor; I don't have much to offer," but you do. You will be amazed again by how much your words, kindness, and thoughts can mean to someone. Everything in life is relative. There are so many people in life that could benefit from you. You can make a difference by helping others, and in doing so, you also help yourself. There is so much joy and pleasure to be gained from giving and being a part of other people's happiness by you contributing to their lives, even in the smallest of ways. So, give freely. You all can find ways to lift others up regardless of how small you think your efforts will be. So even when you think that you are poor, or even if you are, you are still an invaluable part of the process.

So, don't look down on yourself, as Gabriel García Márquez (Gabo), a Colombian author and Nobel Prize recipient in Literature, said:

> "A man must only have the right to look down upon another when he has to help them up." — Gabriel García Márquez.[15,60]

It is still a crucial part of your growth and development as you contribute to society.

You can help others by being part of a non-profit organization. This may be part of a church group or a nondenominational group that supports your interests in enhancing specific causes that may help humanity. You will find that there are numerous opportunities for you to contribute to others' well-being. You do not necessarily have to be in a leadership role to contribute to the organization you are a part of. Nor do you have to be in a position where you have the wherewithal to make large donations of monetary value to these organizations. However, by volunteering your time, expertise, or knowledge and being an ambassador for promoting the cause of the organization's growth and numerous other roles, you will ultimately be helping other people. Therefore, you still are making a significant difference in the lives of so many people.

For example, you may say that you have no money to contribute towards feeding the hungry, you have no transportation to get there, or you cannot be a member of any group probably because you don't have the time, and you simply cannot be of any help. But what if you could get a ride to a facility where they are distributing food to feed the hungry? Then you would be able to contribute by helping that organization to accomplish its mission of providing food for those in need. For example, you could help with food distribution in the kitchen, or maybe in the parking lot with parking. Here you are contributing your time in helping to make a difference. Among the things that are also important for all of us to bear in mind is that many of these organizations run on skeleton staff. They need volunteers in almost every project that they are undertaking to complete their mission.

Without volunteers, most of these organizations would not be able to function adequately and provide the service they are trying to get done. So, you don't have to give a long-term commitment, one where you have to go to meetings, be a part of a group, or contribute money or donations or other things other than your time and effort. But by doing so, you are making an invaluable contribution. All non-profit organizations and related charitable organizations need people to help them. We all can support their cause in so many different ways. And when we do this, it always helps us to reduce our stress. One of the most excellent stress-relieving activities is the feeling of giving to others and knowing that in some small ways, we have made a difference in someone's life.

Bill Gates, an American business magnate, software developer, and philanthropist, spoke about giving back particularly to the less fortunate:

> "We make the future sustainable when we invest in the poor, not when we insist on their suffering." — Bill Gates.[39,61]

It is so important that we are all a part of this; each and every one of us has the capacity to contribute to others, particularly those among us with the greatest means.

Words of Caution or Comments

1. The act of giving is the process through which we uplift others by sharing moments in their lives with our gifts to them without expectation.
2. The process of giving back through organizations often depends on so many to make them function successfully. However, you can always make a difference by volunteering to help.
3. When you help others, you are being charitable by giving, and therefore your reward will always come back to you, not necessarily from those you have helped, but from others.

CHAPTER 19

Conflicts with Friends, Families, Associates, and Society

Family Relationships and Conflicts

It has been said that we may choose our friends or associates, but we do not get to choose our family. But, of course, in most cases, we get to choose our spouses. The stress level that is sometimes experienced by a significant number of people comes directly from their family members. There are so many and varied reasons that result in conflicts that lead to stress: these range from sibling rivalry, different treatment of one sibling over the other, distribution of family inheritance, poor relationships between in-laws and families, separation and divorce, problematic children, and more.

An essential part of any family is two people who are committed legally or not and choose to share lives together. In some countries, same-sex marriage is legal, and in others, it is not. Regardless of the couples involved in the union, they still have issues. Some of these issues often result in significant stress, sometimes more so on one member of the union than the other or both. The nature and the reasons for the conflicts are numerous. Among them are financial, sex, poor communication, job or other extracurricular activities, infidelity, and incompatibility. The approaches taken to resolve these issues are as complex and varied as the problems themselves. What is inevitable is that there is always room for an increased level of stress in these relationships. This is ultimately transferred to other family members involved, and they also have an increased level of stress. Sometimes family counseling might be an option; sometimes, some of the issues may be resolved by medical intervention, a financial advisor; and sometimes, there is no practical or reasonable solution that can save some of these relationships. Therefore, divorce or separation is the best option, with its own level of stress and consequences.

Our children sometimes suffer when there is a dysfunctional relationship that they are a part of. And in as much as we would like to shield them from some of the impacts, some will become victims of failed or failing marriages or other family relationships that involve them. There is no doubt that this creates stress in children that are part of these relationships. There are times when some of these children will try to resolve these things themselves without much success. Some will turn to substance abuse; others become rebellious and even run away from their homes. Some of them may develop a distinct dislike of one or the other member of the relationship. One of the parents may even use them as pawns in the process to achieve their own end. This may have a significant negative impact on the child or children as they may become estranged from one or the other parent.

Added to this, there are sometimes court proceedings that will take on another level of stress for everyone involved and make it more difficult for those involved to have normal lives. The resolution of these issues is generally complex, but most experts agree that both parents' involvement in a child's life is extremely important in their development. Therefore, it is unwise and even cruel for one parent to sabotage their child's relationship by creating an unfavorable or non-existent bond between the child and the other parent. In other words, each parent should do all they can to ensure that their child has a normal relationship with both parents.

With the rate of divorce or separation being as high as it is in most countries, there are many blended families or families where one of the spouses is not the parent of the child or children involved in a newly formed relationship. This sometimes can result in additional stress, particularly when the child is older, approaching early teens. This is also another complex relationship and involves the participation of the new parent or stepparent. The child's other parent needs to create an atmosphere that allows the child to develop an appreciation for all of the parties involved. Sometimes this is extremely difficult to manage for several reasons. As described above, this child may sometimes develop as troubled if they are not given the right support and guidance from all parties involved.

We all can agree that family is an essential component of our lives and is very complex or very simple for some of us. Madonna, an American singer, songwriter, and actress, explained it this way:

> "Family is everything. Family comes first. It's not what I expected it to be, but nothing ever is." — Madonna.[15,90]

As your children grow and become more set in their own ways, with their own personalities and their own way of life, some of them are literally little adults running around your home feeling completely free to do whatever they want without fully understanding the consequences. And sometimes they expect no interference from anyone, and definitely not from their parents. This can often be difficult for some families, who will have to balance what is appropriate and what is not, while trying to love their children, encouraging them to be on the right path and not standing by, and allowing them to do things that will potentially lead to their destruction or have significant negative consequences in their lives. Therefore, sometimes you will have to decide how firm you want to be with your children. Will you draw a line if you find out that your child is using legal or illegal drugs and is going down a destructive path that you have very little control over? Do you call the police? Or do you talk to a counselor? Do you speak to someone at their school or college? And what right do you have to do so? Because they are now adults, and you, regardless of how well-meaning you are, have no right to access their medical information. So, do all that you can to be a part of your children's lives as much as you can. Do not wait until something is wrong, or there is some sign of trouble. Because then it may be too late to find answers to questions that you should have known long ago. Clearly, you can see how this can be extremely difficult and stressful for you and your family.

Stress From Our Children

There is no doubt that our children are our most precious "possession" and, therefore, we must treat them that way. As parents, we are required to love and care for them and instill the virtues that will allow them to be good and productive members of our society. However, sometimes regardless of our best effort, our children become everything that we do not wish for them to be and, in the process, add a lot of stress to our lives and others. Therefore, it is incumbent on parents to create a framework within which children should grow and flourish. Failure to do so is likely to create a generation of adults with myriads of dysfunctions and unacceptable behaviors in society. So as the Bible says:

> "Train up a child in the way he should go, And when he is old, he will not depart from it."
> Proverbs 22:6 — New King James Version

Inasmuch as you love your children, they should not generally determine how your parenting skills apply to them concerning discipline. Remember, you have an obligation to love them always. They don't have to reciprocate your love but rather be the product of a nurturing, safe, and disciplined environment. In the final analysis, you are and should be the major contributors to who they become in society by the actions you enforced, particularly in their early growth and development stages.

Regardless of how we feel about our family, it is essential to remember this, as said by Pope John Paul II, former head of the Catholic Church from 1978 to 2005:

> "As the family goes, so goes the nation and so goes the whole world in which we live." — Pope John Paul II.[15,48]

The family is the unit of our society regardless of how we perceive it.

Societal Relationships and Conflicts

There are many driving forces of stress that are associated with human relationships. Some of them are related to who we are as people. For example, we have different ideas of what is wrong or right, what is acceptable or not, what we want for ourselves and our families, what we want for society and its people, what we consider to be the norms of society, how we believe society should operate, or how we believe society and each person should live their life according to the views we have through the prism of our minds. In fact, concerning relationships, throughout history, in many countries and cultures, there were, and still are, laws or rules that prohibited and still do control many human behaviors or actions.

Some of them are considered acceptable or legal by others, and some are unacceptable or possibly violating depending on where you live in the world.

Some of these behaviors that lead to significant stress are marriages or relationships between different races, different cultures, same-sex/or LGBTQIA+ members, individuals of different religions, individuals considered to have "significant age differences," and between different classes (rich /poor/culture/tribe/group/etc.). The extent to which these factors cause great stress has been well documented. Some of these range from people who have been banished from their families or their specific group/tribe, beaten, or murdered. Some individuals who are involved in some of these relationships will literally live a secret life or closeted life, sometimes for years or a lifetime. The level of stress experienced by anyone living their life in this manner is undoubtedly beyond the imagination of most of us who never had to live this way. It is hard to say that it is a choice that each person or couple makes to live the way they do because these issues are incredibly complex. There are so many factors that influence each person's personal decisions to live their life the way they want and decide when and who they choose to be part of their decision. Among the challenges in some of these relationships are children and even adults that are affected tremendously, adding to the complexity of challenges that some of these relationships may face, regardless of whether the relationship is right or wrong, and of course, who has the right to make that judgment.

An extremely important point to be made in discussing these relationships is that numerous relationships fit those mentioned above that are "model relationships," and the people involved could not be happier. In fact, in some cases, and probably because we are all people of the same human race, they are happier and more successful in those relationships than those that some may consider acceptable in their eyes. The simple truth is what works for you may not work for me. Though we have so much in common, we do not have to have the same things you have or live the same way you do.

My point here is not to discuss the complexity of each of these relationships but to highlight the fact that regardless of the view you hold, and for whatever reason, each of these relationships means something to somebody. So I leave you with a quote from The Prophet, Khalil Gibran, a Lebanese-American writer, poet, and visual artist:

> "And think not you can direct the course of love, for love, if it finds you worthy, directs your course."
>
> "Love has no other desire but to fulfill itself." — Khalil Gibran.[15,103]

This is the way he saw it. The power of love is often a force that cannot be overcome by most of us. Not even the fear of death will stop some of us.

Relationship conflicts are significant, as described in this chapter; also important are the conflicts that occur from time to time among individuals for numerous reasons. There is almost always a significant amount of stress associated with these conflicts. Some may have developed because of poor communication, misrepresentation by one or more of the people involved, misunderstanding or misrepresentation, or people's inability to understand or to ascertain all the facts surrounding the reasons for disagreement or conflict. The list, of course, is endless. Where possible, it is advisable to do all we can to avoid unnecessary conflicts. Some of the strategies mentioned here in this book for relieving stress will also help ensure that. It's also important to know that you don't have to win every conflict you are involved in or every argument or fight or disagreement. Sometimes the temptation is powerful to prevail in all circumstances. However, in the end, you may still be fighting a losing battle in the process with lots of wasted energy on things that are essentially trivial over the long run but may appear to be of great significance when you're involved in them. Rev. Dr. Martin Luther King Jr. said this:

> "The ultimate measure of a man is not where he stands in moments of comfort and convenience, but where he stands at times of challenge and controversy." — Dr. Martin Luther King Jr.[15,96]

We are all directed by our minds, and we determine how we react to the buttons of our lives that others get to push.

Never Forget the Value of Friends and Associations

Never forget the value of friendships and relationships. They are priceless, particularly those people who were there in your corners all the time no matter what, stress or no stress. Friendship is priceless. No man is an island. We all need to have friends in our lives and good relationships. Your friends are people with whom you can talk and say anything. Don't let them get away; keep them close to you. You don't need ten or twenty people to be friends with. You need a few people, maybe just enough that you could count on one hand. That is OK. They are an incredible and an essential part of your life.

Muhammad Ali, an American professional boxer, activist, entertainer, and philanthropist, explained friendship as follows:

> "Friendship is the hardest thing in the world to explain. It's not something you learn in school. But if you haven't learned the meaning of friendship, you really haven't learned anything." — Muhammad Ali.[15,89]

We have heard it said that each one teaches one. Sometimes relationships can be like that. Whatever you are doing in life, there are times when you are at some point that you may be a little lost, or you probably need some guidance that can make the difference in whether you succeed and even reduce the amount of stress that you are facing to accomplish your task. The proverbial big brother or sister can genuinely make a difference by taking you on a new path.

Sometimes we see it in the form of mentorship. **Mentorship** is an essential process as it relates to stress. Mentors' guidance can be a life-changing event for many who are struggling to find their way in life or pursuing their endeavors. It is also beneficial for those who are not necessarily having difficulties in what they are focusing on but are trying to advance and get to a higher level of excellence. Mentors can indeed provide the framework in which the mentee can grow more successfully. This type of mentor-mentee relationship can eliminate or reduce many potential pitfalls and the trial and error that an inexperienced person likely would face without having the benefit of a mentor. Therefore, mentorship is a crucial component in helping to reduce stress in a lot of ways.

An essential factor in this relationship is the realization that everyone can be a mentor at some point in their life. The basic principle is we can all learn from each other if we allow others to teach us. Suppose someone else is more experienced or has more knowledge than another, then mentorship has the potential to be of benefit not just to the mentor but to the mentee in terms of both learning from each other and reducing their level of stress. It doesn't always have to be an extended period of mentorship; it may take the form of simple advice and encouragement given to someone in need. This also works for both the mentor and mentee, helping others in different ways by creating a relationship that enhances their chance of being better at whatever they are pursuing.

You may see similar relationships in business and professional settings as well. This also can help in developing mutual trust and benefit to those that are involved. The camaraderie of sharing information, sharing knowledge, giving advice, and encouragement that can create new pathways that may never have existed before or without those relationships or collaborative efforts. When these exist, they will make a difference by decreasing the amount of stress those involved are experiencing, making it more likely that each one rises to a higher level than without these efforts.

Everyone Has Limits

Sometimes there is a limit to how far you can go or how much you can accomplish in trying to help others or getting the best out of them. We often put a lot of stress on ourselves simply by expecting others to have a level of performance or expertise in doing tasks or responsibilities that we hope they will perform and sometimes do so flawlessly. Or sometimes, we expect others to have certain character traits, core values, or moral principles. Unfortunately, we often fail to realize that everyone has limits. Therefore, even though you are requesting or expecting someone to do something or have specific conduct, and they have the greatest desire and intention of meeting your requirements well, they are simply not capable of delivering what you're asking or expecting of them. Now, it doesn't matter whether you pay them more, encourage them, make them feel inadequate, or whatever strategies you may use. If they do not have the ability or the capacity to do or be whatever you want, they will not complete the task you are requesting or meet your expectation.

So, understand people's limitations and skillsets and know that we all have different strengths and weaknesses, particularly if you are in a leadership position. Know that everyone cannot and will not do the same task effectively or has the same character as the other person. There are limits to what each person can do or be, so it is pointless stressing yourself to the degree where you are so frustrated and angry because people are not who you expect them to be.

The next point here is also to understand that we should not allow ourselves and our limitations to prevent others from accomplishing what they are capable of or to take away from them the opportunity to do something that they will do if given a chance and the appropriate conditions necessary to allow learning and improve their growth and development. This is often a challenge for so many people, particularly in a leadership role, who believe that they know the limitations of people and can determine what they are capable of doing and what they know. Limitations of this nature are sometimes based on only what they can see, or on their bias, prejudice, or their own innate limitations of what they are capable of doing. They may use this as a barometer of trying to determine what others are capable of doing.

The process of assessing others and oneself is a challenging concept. Still, it allows everyone to think of themselves as a potential guide to getting the best out of each one but not being the ultimate person determining what a person's ability or limitations are. So allow ourselves to be wrong sometimes and know that we don't always have all the answers. We certainly are not capable of doing everything as perfectly ourselves as someone who is not an expert in something that we may not have been trained or may not have had the level of expertise or capability of doing.

Relationships in communities among community members and community leaders can build better and stronger bonds that help galvanize people around a common cause, goals, and aspirations, leading to a more productive society. The society with common goals and aspirations is often driven by people who have the desire to succeed and make each other better, creating a community of more like-minded individuals that will enhance each other's desire to make each other better. Conceptually, this will generate more optimism and greater responsibilities of each individual, leading to people living their lives in a happier and more fulfilling way. Needless to say, the happier you are, the less stress you will have.

Know the Wishes of Those That are Silent

There are times when family members pass away or cannot communicate their wishes because of illness or incapacitation. The deceased or incapacitated individuals' wishes must be honored by family members who were designated or assumed responsibility. The level of stress becomes evident and sometimes extremely significant, depending on how much interaction or how close each member of a given family is as a whole. There are other factors, such as did these family members in question have anything worth fighting for, such as an estate of significant value, real or perceived? If they do, it is not uncommon to see a high level of conflict. Suppose there is not much to be gained by anyone from the estate. In that case, the person in charge, the executor, or the assumed leader of the family, will be the one often taking care of everything while others tend to drift off in their own way and assume little or no responsibility. This can lead to a lot of stress on the person taking care of their loved one's estate.

Therefore, it is crucial that each person, whatever their status in life is, make their wishes known to their family, particularly those who are likely to be in charge when you are no longer here because of death or illness or before you become incapacitated. This may be in the form of a last will or living trust usually related to estate planning and settlement.

In addition, there are advance directives (living will, healthcare proxy, power of attorney, etc.) which are legal documents that provide the framework of your wishes or how decisions should be made about end-of-life care (healthcare, long-term care, etc.) before incapacitation or your passing.

Both estate planning and advance directives are essential and should be part of everyone's life. These will result in a significant reduction of stress, anxiety, and cost for those who are involved. Unfortunately, these things are often very difficult to address and talk about because nobody wants to talk about their death and funeral. Therefore, people tend to stay away from these types of conversations. However, it is essential to have them.

Sometimes, bank accounts and other assets are left hanging around, and one or more siblings or relatives may feel that they have the exclusive right to them. But sometimes, because their name is on the bank account or they may live in the house of the affected family member, they suddenly believe that the house and all the money in the accounts belong to them. Now, this may be true. However, it is essential for each family member or the owner of anything of value to make it clear how they want their assets to be distributed and to whom. It is commonly known that when it comes to an individual's assets, as long as it has some value, there is always the potential for conflicts and disputes as you try to resolve basically who gets what and why. And as always, if there is nothing to gain, most family members will go their separate ways and leave one or two people to take care of everything by themselves.

Caregivers' Stress Overload

The saying "once a man, twice a child" is generally accepted as the need for a child to be taken care of from birth to adulthood to a state of physical, mental, and to some degree financial independence. However, once that status is reached, often when older, the adult may regress to a reduction or absence of these things or factors which make them independent or capable of taking care of their needs. Hence, they will have the need to be taken care of by others, therefore, starting the cycle over again.

Caregivers of all ages are faced with tremendous stress taking care of those who are physically, mentally, or psychosocially impaired or financially challenged. Some of the questions often need addressing are: how does one deal with the many factors that compound or exacerbate the stress level, what are the solutions available, and how can one effectively access these resources?

One may be entrusted into the role of a caregiver by virtue of sudden illness, accidents, bankruptcy, loss of a significant breadwinner, mental illness, dementia, safety concerns, congenital disorder, birth defects, medical negligence, and a never-ending list of other possibilities.

One of the things that can cause stress in caregivers is that they may not have the financial wherewithal or the mental and physical requirements to be a sustained caregiver for anyone. Sometimes they need help: they may not be able to take care of their parent, take time off, or suspend their job if they have any job or understand the social networks and available supports that may benefit them. Even for those that are financially capable and have the resources to deal with their loved ones who need their care, the act of being an active participant as a caregiver weighs heavily on any and everyone who is involved at almost any stage.

Here are some possible solutions and things that might be helpful to bear in mind in reducing your stress concerning functioning as caregivers.

1. Be prepared for this possibility rather than waiting until you are dealing with the reality of it. Advance directives and estate planning (see above) are often very helpful.
2. There are available long-term care and disability insurances, some private and governmental insurance policies, which provide benefits that will be helpful. These, of course, have

to be purchased or added to your policy in anticipation of long-term care of your loved ones or yourself.

3. The need for social workers, case managers, family or primary care physicians, and consultants can play critical roles in helping to facilitate more easy transitions into the role of caregivers.
4. If you are in a position where you are designing, building, or buying your home, think of making or facilitating handicap accessibility or create a plan for a potentially easy structural conversion to that.
5. If you are a caregiver, make time for yourself, get help, rotate activities or responsibilities with other siblings, friends, or family where possible.
6. Sometimes as a family member, you have to come to the realization that you cannot do it, and as difficult as this choice may be, you have to transition your loved one to a facility or to others for their care.
7. Be cognizant of the physical, mental or emotional, and financial impact this is likely to have on you as a caregiver.

This section about caregivers is a small synopsis of an important and complex topic that causes tremendous stress. Many have to deal with the challenges of being a caregiver for those they truly want the best for. However, sometimes they are unable to provide that. Please educate yourself about this issue to reduce its impact on your life and reduce your stress level.

Words of Caution or Comments

1. The relationships between families and their members are critical because the family is a unit of primary significance and forms the core unit of our society.
2. It is hard for most people to monitor their own lives and do all they need to do to succeed. There is simply not enough time to burden yourself with the issues of other people's lives unless you are of help to them.
3. Friendship is that part of us that is complete when we no longer worry about who we are, who we are with, what we say, or even why.
4. Always protect your friend. They should never have to lie for you, need immunity because of you, be in danger, or die for you so that you can be whole.
5. Cherish the friends you have had for ages, but always open yourself to accepting new ones. It is part of how we grow and mutually enhance the lives of others and ourselves.
6. If your only objective in life is to win in conflict resolution, then your humanity is compromised. Allow others the option of not being victimized by your actions.
7. Do the best you can in conflict resolution to allow everyone to win or at the very least allow for compromise rather than one person walking away feeling like a winner and the others feeling like losers.
8. You may be successful doing everything you can throughout your life, or at least, you may believe so. However,

sometimes no one notices you until someone points to you. Find yourself a mentor and be a mentor to others.

9. We may not be able to eliminate all the stress from conflicts related to our loved ones' passing. However, we can certainly take actions to decrease disputes between family members, which is worth doing.
10. Everyone has limits. No one can give you more than they are capable of, even if they want to do so. So, do not stress yourselves trying to go beyond empty.

CHAPTER 20

I Do Not Want to Talk About Sex

Now, how many times have you heard this, or how many times have you said this, or probably have heard it said by someone else? Many people are afraid of talking about race, racism, politics, or religion in most societies. However, sex is often right up there as one of the things most people are just not comfortable talking about with anyone. The interesting thing is that there is potentially so much stress associated with sex. These may present in relation to sex or sexual intercourse, a sexual relationship, sexuality, sexual orientation, sexual expression, who is having sex, different types of sex, societal expectations of sex, cultural norms of sex, how sex and religion affect you, sexual abuse, and just a myriad of different sex-related issues and views. There are so many different variations of what is considered normal versus what is deemed inappropriate or just harmful or wrong or unacceptable.

So, where does one begin in addressing the issues of sex as it relates to stress? With such a wide variation in differences among individuals and cultures, whatever I say here will be applicable only in part or some instances, or not at all to some people. In this chapter, I hope to raise your consciousness level and allow you to think about a subject matter that is so important but often remains the elephant in the room that will not go away.

Many couples are in committed relationships yet have never had a meaningful or in-depth discussion about sex. Often, neither party is generally comfortable discussing sex or sexual relationship as it applies to them for so many different reasons. Sometimes this could be as simple as their views and what is culturally acceptable to them. For example, will one partner consider the other strange or perverted if their significant other is interested in using sex toys and/or exploring various types of sex included but not limited to vaginal, oral, anal, or others? Which of these, if any, would they deem inappropriate or considered deserving of some penalty, and why? Now, the answer to this will vary significantly between individuals and between different cultures and different norms. I am not here to tell you what is normal for you, what is right for you, what you should be doing, or what type of sex you should have. But what I would like you to do is have discussions about these things to understand what your partner wants of you or expects so that there is clarity in your sexual relationship. For example, some people may believe that they should not read a book about sex or information about sex. Many refrain simply from doing that. Or, if they should look at a video or literature about sex, then the question becomes, is that pornography, and where do they draw the line? Or is it something that could enhance their sexual relationships?

In some instances, people's culture or religion prevents them from appearing or dressing in a manner that is considered to be sexy or provocative, even in their homes or bedrooms. In addition, there are certain positions when having sex that, for one reason or another, may not be acceptable to one partner or the other or one culture or the other and is just considered inappropriate.

Sometimes some sexual acts or just sexual intercourse, or the way it is performed, may bring back memories to you or your partner of previous experience with sex or sexual abuse or other traumatic experiences of some form related to sex. Discussing these things openly and honestly with your partner will be helpful and can significantly affect how pleasurable each partner's experiences are sexually.

Some people believe that if they were to go to a store that sells sex-related items, that would be against everything they believe in and, therefore, would be an embarrassment or sinful for them even to consider doing that. And who knows who may see them going to that store?

So now the question becomes, how does one learn about sex when they have had no experience and do not wish to talk about sex with anyone? Compounding the problem is that some partners in relationships often know very little about their sexual preferences or desires. Sometimes they may even lack knowledge about how their body should function concerning sex, how their own sexuality or sexual organs function, or what are the expectations of their partner with respect to sex or their sexual organ are. For example, what is normal about the female genitalia or the male genitalia? What is abnormal? And how do you know whether your partner's genitals are normal or not? And if it is not normal, what can you do about it? Should you consult therapists or a medical doctor, or are you willing to discuss this openly with a therapist or other professionals?

The reality is that most people are so afraid of what people may think of them once they begin to talk about sex. Because the perception is that they may be judged by the information that they will be discussing. As a result of this, most people do not talk about sex because they don't want to be judged or be considered to be perverted or to be doing something that is not acceptable. One strange thing about this is that even in some committed relationships, each party is just afraid of talking to the other about sex and all the issues surrounding sex or sexuality, sexual act, sexual relationship, what is pleasurable, and what is not. These are all essential things that must be discussed.

Now, whatever sexual relationship one may be involved in, there will be stress regarding the relationship if these things are not dealt with. Sometimes it may be simple questions like: is sexual intercourse painful, why is it painful, is it pleasurable, why is it pleasurable, or not? What positions are better for one person may not be OK for the other person, and if it is not better for the other person, why not? Understanding or knowing these things will sometimes determine how each partner reacts in a sexual relationship or sexual intercourse. These answers are important and often can have a significant negative or positive impact on the relationship.

How one dresses is often something that is also part of sexuality, and if one dresses in a way that conceals their body or in a way that they are less sexually attractive, why is that person doing that? Is it because of cultural norms, or is it because that person doesn't want to have sex? Or does someone get to bed at a certain time and is always tired or always sleepy and has to get up early and go to work the next day and therefore cannot or does not have enough time to interact with their partner? All these things may be ways of avoiding sex or attempting to deal with other underlying medical issues that make sex difficult. Once a partner is avoiding sex, there are reasons for that, and those must be discussed or at least explored to find solutions. There are other times when people will basically just wing it—they are in a committed relationship, but they will not talk to anyone about any difficulties they have. They are not going to discuss their sex life. Instead, they will try and do whatever feels comfortable.

But the point I want to make is that if you allow yourself to talk about these issues openly with professionals or with people who can help you, then chances are you will be able to reduce the amount of stress in your life as it relates to sex. Sex is one of the most important aspects of any relationship. If it is not acceptable, it is just a matter of time before the relationship fails, regardless of the type of relationship and all the other structures or factors that may be working perfectly fine.

The other side of this spectrum—(of I don't want to talk about sex)—is that so many people have read and learned extensively about sex. They probably know most things to be known about sex, and yet they still have stress. This may be partly because of their approach to sex and their own sexuality. This may also have to do with what is acceptable to them in their religion and culture and how they indulged in sex. As a result, some of them stress about casual sex, promiscuity, unprotected sex, illicit sex, and a range of other types of sex or related sex acts leading to stress.

Additionally, sometimes there are medical issues that create added stress between partners or each individual. This may range from erectile dysfunction, premature ejaculation, inability to reach a climax, painful sexual intercourse (both male and female), physical pain, or physical limitations that are not directly related to sex but impact sex. There are also psychological or psychiatric issues, infection, sexually transmitted disease, poor hygiene, and a host of other things, including factors that are stressors that tend to get in the way of sex.

These things can affect just about every relationship in different ways depending on the nature of sex, sex-related issues, or their specific impact, resulting in tremendous stress for everyone involved.

One of the most significant stressors related to sex is sexuality, sexual orientation, and sexual expression. There are so many different ways that individuals may classify themselves with respect to sex, sexuality, or sexual orientation. The challenge is that each individual has to come to terms with their own identity and how that fits into the world they live in and how their decisions or status might affect the way they are perceived. Also, the way that society, to some degree, will accept or reject them for who they decide to be or who they are will be a factor. For this reason, in part, many people will live a life that is inconsistent with their sexual orientation or their sexuality, resulting in constant stress. This issue, of course, is very complex. I came across two articles: one describes forty-six terms of sexual attraction, behavior, and orientation. The second article has sixty-four terms that describe gender identity and expression (Mere Abrams, Healthline) [24,25]. By now, some of you may have lost track of the progression of the acronym for lesbian, gay, and transgender to where it is LGBTQIA+. Meaning: lesbian, gay, bisexual, transgender, queer/questioning, intersex, and agender/asexual, with the "plus" referring to other self-identifying members of the community who do not identify as heterosexual. Numerous other acronyms are similar to this or an extension of it. The point here is that there are many ways people identify themselves, their sexuality or orientation, how they classify their gender, or how they see themselves as a person. This can lead to a life where one does not fit into society's normal expectations, leading to a stressful life for some individuals as they try to fit into the broader community as a whole. Complicating the matter is each person can and will change their status of who they are or how they identify themselves from time to time.

Words of Caution or Comments

1. It is not my intention to tell you what is appropriate for you regarding sexuality or sex or what you should do in your bedroom or private life.

2. Sex is a complex topic, as it is difficult for people to talk about and is challenging to write about. However, it is my intention to encourage people to explore the various and different options of what may be possible to improve their sex life. This begins with a frank and open discussion about the subject matter.
3. Unless there is communication regarding sex about what is acceptable to each other, then and only then can the framework be established to help find resolutions for sexual-related issues that are so critical in impacting our lives and creating significant stress.
4. This chapter is not intended to endorse any particular type of sex or one way of doing or having sex but rather to ask people to allow themselves to be free to discuss an important aspect of their life that can significantly reduce the amount of stress that they are experiencing.
5. Sex and sexuality are essential parts of every meaningful relationship. However, understanding sex, the consequence of having sex, the reasons that sex impacts our lives, how sex occurs, the limitations of having sex, the health concern, and others must also be explored and addressed as they are critically important.

CHAPTER 21

Find Your Spiritual and Political Center

Is Your Religion Stressing You Out?

Religion has played a significant role in our lives throughout the world. For many, this is a way to find comfort, a place of order, a place to be with your inspirational leader, to connect or be in unison with a force or a source of something bigger and more significant than yourself, or a community you can totally or entirely relate to. Therefore, this often results in different ways of people connecting and subscribing to their own diverse beliefs. In addition, this allows significant relief of stress experienced by the participants being part of their chosen group or religion.

Although there are many different religious groups and non-religious people who practice certain beliefs, it is essential that you find your spiritual center. Now, this will mean different things to different people. Some people are religious, and others are not. Some have different ways that they worship, and that is personal to them. You know what connects you with your inner self or what allows you to connect to a force that is greater than yourself. And that is important to you. It is an important aspect of who you are in the culture within that group or the community you belong to or believe in. It is also essential that you follow your guide, whatever that is, as this is part of your core value or core beliefs. Your presence and participation in your religion or group may often resolve or reduce some of the stresses you face by connecting with the community that you feel you could bond with most closely.

So, make sure that you connect with your religious group or your universal group or whatever you call it, or whatever it is you are connecting with. Those groups, those people, are essential to you. They are a part of who you are. Ensure that you treasure that aspect of your life because that is an integral part of who you are. Resolving some of the challenges and stresses in your life by connecting with your inner self, with your God, or your highest spiritual leader will be of benefit.

Not everyone belongs to a religious group. Many of you have no religious belief. Some of you connect to your inner self or the universe or no one or anything. Some people meditate. Some people just find other ways to link to other groups that are non-religious or nondenominational and become a part of those groups or cultures. For them, this can also be a source of relieving their stress or level of anxiety related to stress.

There are many religious groups in the world. The Pew Research Center lists twelve major religious groups worldwide, among many other groups.[29]

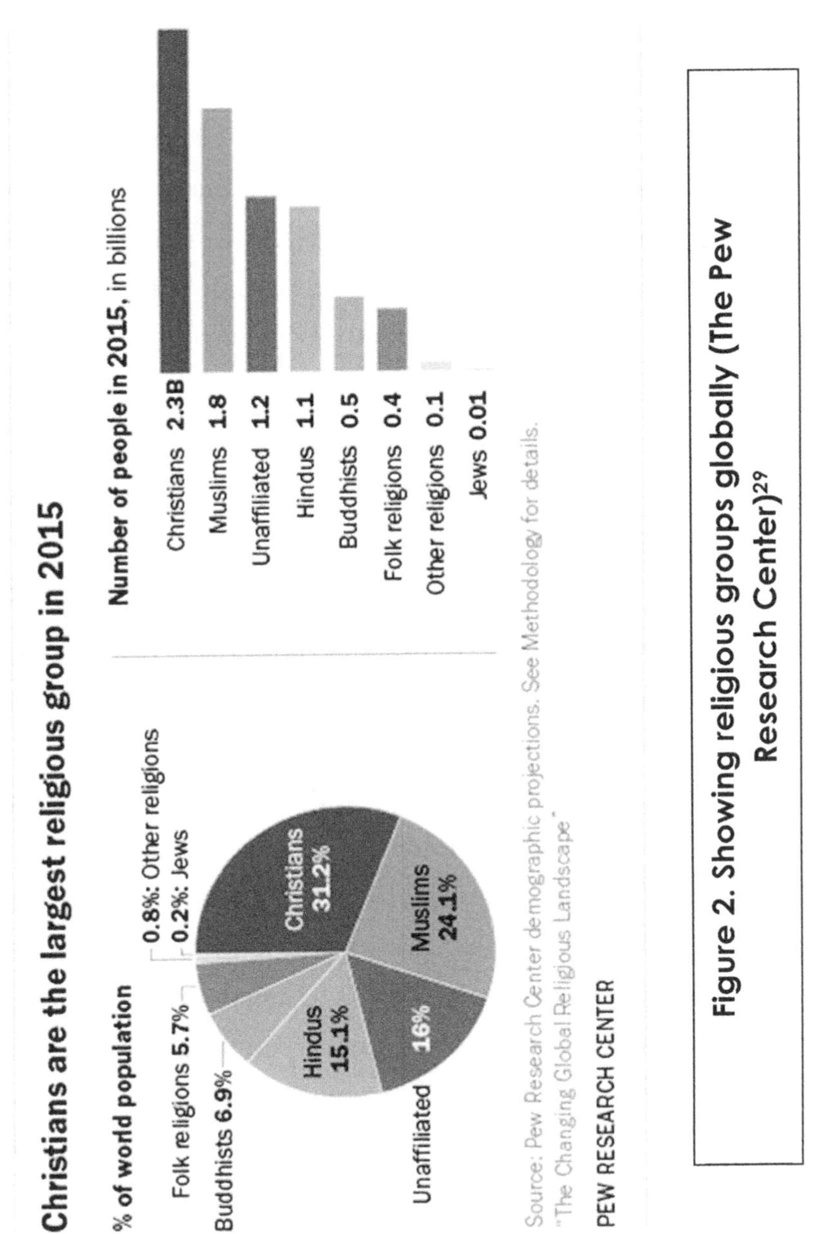

Figure 2. Showing religious groups globally (The Pew Research Center)[29]

These groups are Christianity, Islam, Hinduism, Buddhism, Sikhism, Taoism, Judaism, Confucianism, Bahá'í, Shinto, Jainism, and Zoroastrianism.

Connecting to religion, religious groups, spirituality, or any groups that create a community of like-mindedness will help reduce the level of stress the members of those groups are experiencing, even though there are many similarities and differences between religious groups and other groups. Therefore, religion has a significant role in all of our lives and impacts us in so many different ways, not only in reducing stress but also in many other ways beyond this book's scope.

However, one thing to bear in mind is that over time each religion and the subgroup within it changes or becomes something that resembles what it used to be. So, we find, for example, many different types of Baptist churches or Pentecostal churches, or Wesleyan Methodist Churches. Also, the parishioners or members change from one religion to another or from one group within a specific religion to another. They try to find what is appropriate for them and how they want to worship. And, of course, a significant number of the world's population has embraced no religion or no affiliation with any religion at all. Therefore, as each of you strives to find ways to deal with resolving or improving your stress level, as important as religion is, sometimes, it can be a source for or a reason that creates stress for some people. This often occurs as some of you grapple with your own religious faith and try to figure out what is right for you or if you are on the right path. However, this is not unusual when you look at all the different religions, of which the largest is Christianity, which accounts for about 30 percent of the world's religion. This means that about 70 percent of the world rejects Christianity. Hinduism represents approximately 15 percent, nondenominational about 16 percent, Judaism about 0.2 percent, and Zoroastrianism 0.03 percent.[22,29] These numbers show that religion in the world is pretty divided. And that even for significant groups of religion, they are rejected by the vast majority of the world's population.

Religion certainly means different things to different people. However, we probably all can agree with the fourteenth Dalai Lama, currently the highest spiritual leader of Tibet:

> "Whether one believes in a religion or not, and whether one believes in rebirth or not, there isn't anyone who doesn't appreciate kindness and compassion." — Dalai Lama.[15,30]

Therefore, it is not surprising if you are having thoughts about whether your religion is right for you. Know that this is a normal progression to go through. In fact, we all should allow ourselves not to be so confined by any of them. You should allow yourself the freedom to change from religion to religion if you see that it fits your ideals or if that religion no longer suits you or your needs, or if it is no longer consistent with what you believe, or you simply see things differently. It is then OK for you to say to yourself that this is not working anymore and that you need to find something different.

It is also OK for you to say you don't know what you want now, or right now, or you do not wish to have any religious connection.

That is also OK. Now, I cannot tell you which religion to choose or not to choose or tell you to leave your religion. But what I can encourage all of you to do is have the freedom to think, the freedom to know that you have the power that your beautiful mind gave you to make choices and feel free without being stressed. You don't have to hold on to one religion for the rest of your life and see that as the only religion that exists for you.

Is Your Politics Stressing You Out?

Politics is almost everywhere, in every culture and every country. There are numerous and different political systems. This is coupled with the idea that human beings will have many similarities and differences wherever we are in the world. Our political systems or our politics for generations have created tremendous stress on its people. Countless people have died and suffered greatly, and are still suffering, in part because of the political systems that they have lived in or are currently living in. Some of the greatest injustices, cruelties, or atrocities have been done in the name of politics and sometimes religion. The words of former President Abraham Lincoln echo loudly:

> "Nearly all men can stand adversity, but if you want to test a man's character, give him power."
> — Abraham Lincoln.[39,59]

Very often, we have heard it said, never trust a politician. In addition to the injustices and atrocities that have been committed in the name of politics, there are less painful experiences by people in their respective political systems. However, these can be stressful for many individuals and often lead to significant discontent and emotional suffering in society. People will choose their political leaders or have an affinity to them, usually because of many factors. These may range from a shared belief in core values, ideologies, or their own selfish gain, and sometimes no specific reason at all. Now, because we have our own idea of what we believe in that is different from others, even within the same family, there is room for disagreement to exist, or at least there should be. Unless you see things differently than former President Thomas Jefferson did:

> "I never considered a difference of opinion in politics, in religion, in philosophy, as cause for withdrawing from a friend." — Thomas Jefferson.[15,33]

Sometimes these can lead to significant conflict between individuals or family members, different political groups, or party members. The extent to which these can be resolved amicably and with mutual respect is often highly dependent on the political or group leaders and the atmosphere they create. They have the power to incite violence, create fear or discontent, facilitate greater division between individual groups or equally; these leaders can bring the different groups together peacefully and create harmony among them. This, therefore, allows the leaders to have the capacity to inflict great stress on their desired target. But of course, worse than that, they have the power to control the minds of those who will hang onto their every word. With the power to control them, they can lead them down a path of destruction, even resulting in their own demise.

The late Sen. John McCain III, an American statesman and United States Navy officer, summed up the effects of religion and politics this way:

> "The political tactics of division and slander are not our values. They are corrupting influences on religion and politics, and those who practice them in the name of religion or in the name of the Republican Party or in the name of America shame our faith, our party and our country." — John McCain.[31,32]

Yes, it is OK to say amen!

Words of Caution or Comments

1. It is wise never to be so inflexible to hold on to any religious or political view that is so strong that it completely engulfs your mind—that has the power to destroy you.
2. Allow yourself the option to think or to see the possibility of other things. Always have some flexibility in your thoughts.

3. It does not matter how good your current group or community makes you feel. Give yourself a chance to go from feeling good to better or even your exceptional best.
4. You have the ability and power to see things differently by merely opening your mind and allowing others to teach you as much as you teach them.

CHAPTER 22

Get Professional Help

Sometimes we try to solve problems or fix them ourselves, and we often do this because it is more convenient. We do not want to ask for help, nor do we feel the need to do so. But, there are times when professional service is not just something that should be thought about but should be incorporated into your possible solutions. It is so important to resolve some of the issues you are facing, and you may be unable to settle them independently.

There are times when things are so overwhelming that you cannot deal with them all by yourself. Therefore, you have to get professional help—sometimes a medical doctor, a psychologist, or other therapists. These are professionals who could help you, someone who could listen to you more objectively. In addition, there are likely to be occasions in your life where you need to get additional help because it is essential to have resolutions of some of the issues that are no longer minor but have progressed. This could require treatment that may include comprehensive counseling, medications, or specialized therapies such as cognitive-behavioral or biofeedback therapy.

Also, there are times when you will need some additional help, which you may not be able to harness by yourself or with your friends and family. Hence, you have to go outside of that circle to receive the help you need. Now, that is crucial. It does not mean that you're crazy or that your world is falling apart because you need to talk to a psychiatrist or psychologist. You will be OK, but you must get the proper help you need because, without it, you and your family may not be able to move from the state that you are in and transform it into a better way of living.

This is a significant step in the process of recovery or improvement of your stress level. It may take all the courage that you have. Robert (Bob) Marley, OM, was a Jamaican singer, songwriter, and musician who said this that can be helpful in difficult times:

> "You never know how strong you are, until being strong is your only choice." — Bob Marley.[15,54]

So, make sure that you get help when you need it or when others around you are saying to you that they think you need it. Listen to them because very often, they can see you more than you can see yourself. They can see things that you are doing that you cannot understand, see, or interpret. So, as difficult as it may be to accept the realization that you may be giving up your control to others, you have to understand, listen, and trust your friends and family to be your best advisors and supporters.

Princess Diana, Princess of Wales, was a member of the British royal family who spoke about caring for each other on a larger scale. It definitely starts with the people that are closest to us.

> "Everyone of us needs to show how much we care for each other and, in the process, care for ourselves." — Princess Diana.[15,39]

The last thing you would want to do is sit around and tell yourself that you can deal with your condition and have everything under your control, when in fact, you don't. Take the time to listen. Make sure that you utilize all the services that are available to you to get help.

I have included a chapter in this book about the anatomy of stress (chapter 1b). This is in part to allow everyone who reads this book to understand that stress is not something that is just in our minds, but there is a scientific basis for stress. There are physical structures that are associated with modulating and controlling stress. As I mentioned, there is a need to see professionals and/or medical providers. It is essential to talk with your primary care doctor or medical provider to assess any possible stress you believe you are experiencing, particularly when you are unsure about exactly what is happening to you. There are numerous reasons that will cause an individual to experience symptoms that are consistent with stress. First, there are possible physical considerations related to the anatomical causes of stress in your body. These include but are not limited to your brain or other areas of your body. Suppose there is malfunctioning because of disease processes or some hormonal imbalance. In that case, these can create symptoms similar to those experienced by an individual who is stressed but has no direct correlation with abnormal body structures. In other words, there is no obvious disease process that is causing the stress, which then will allow the focus to be on other external factors where the body still plays its role but is not the cause of the symptoms one is experiencing.

For example, suppose a disease process results in your body's cortisol level not being appropriately adjusted. In that case, that may lead to a sense of heightened stress levels or some variation of it. This is likely to occur even with no apparent external factor, for example, finances or job-related stressors, among others. Therefore, the need for a medical evaluation to eliminate direct medical causes from consideration is essential. So that if there is an underlying illness or medical reason other than external factors causing general stress, then those can be addressed. There may be times when additional studies or diagnostic tests will be necessary to evaluate and treat your stress. For example, you may need imaging studies such as an MRI of the brain, ultrasound of adrenal glands, or laboratory tests to determine specific hormonal levels. Therefore, having a comprehensive medical evaluation is an essential part of stress evaluation, treatment, and stress management.

Another important reason to see or get professional help is a need for obtaining prescription medications that can sometimes be very useful in controlling some of the associated signs and symptoms of stress. These conditions include psychiatric disorders or mood disorders often associated with stress signs and symptoms. In some cases, only limited short-term treatment is necessary, particularly during acute and episodic acute stress, whereas some individuals may benefit from longer-term medication treatment. In addition to prescribing medications for mood disorders or related psychiatric symptoms, your medical provider can also treat other numerous medical conditions (examples: pain, diabetes, heart disease, etc.) that may cause exacerbation of your stress level. Once they are better managed, your stress level will also be improved. Therefore, having a comprehensive medical evaluation and treatment can make a significant difference in your stress level.

However we look at stress treatment and its management, it is not easy, particularly when you are confronted with multiple factors affecting you and your struggle to find solutions. Still, sometimes nothing seems to be working well. It is frustrating. It can happen to even the best of us. Even one of the greatest sports figures of all time struggled his way to success. National Basketball Association legend and businessman Michael Jordan said this:

> "I've missed more than 9,000 shots in my career. I've lost almost 300 games. Twenty-six times, I've been trusted to take the game-winning shot and missed. I've failed over and over and over again in my life. And that is why I succeed." — Michael Jordan.[79,80]

So, whatever you do, keep trying and follow the principles outlined in this book and others. You will succeed!

Words of Caution or Comments

1. Stress in the acute, chronic, or episodic state is closely associated with depression, anxiety, and other psychiatric disorders. Therefore, you must obtain a professional opinion or treatment to deal with any related condition or feeling that you may experience with stress.
2. I will leave a number at the end of this chapter and in the reference section for suicide prevention, as well as websites.[23]
3. Make sure to use this number if you ever feel so down or depressed that you are contemplating or thinking about committing suicide.

Call the National Suicide Prevention Lifeline

"Anyone can become overwhelmed. If you or a loved one is having thoughts of suicide, call the confidential toll-free National Suicide Prevention Lifeline at 1-800-273-TALK (8255), available 24 hours a day, 7 days a week. Lifeline chat is a service available to everyone."

U.S. Department of Health and Human Services
National Institutes of Health
NIH Publication No. 19-MH-8109

If you are outside of the USA, visit: www.befrienders.org or www.IASP.info

CONCLUSION

My Parting Thoughts

Stress is indeed a significant issue in our society today, wherever you are in the world. It stretches across cultures, races, classes, geographical locations, and religions and affects everyone, even those that think they are in their own world. It will find you. In this book, I have given many options, asked many questions, and provided pathways to help prevent and reduce the stress one is experiencing. There are many things that can be helpful for stress reduction and prevention. In this book, you will find three main categories that I have described as necessary to be a part of every stress reduction and prevention program, whether it is used for self-application by an individual or a group intended for a therapeutic process supervised by professionals. The need for each person to optimize their chances of reducing their stress level cannot be overemphasized. Also, I have provided you with forty-plus actions that are part of those three categories. They are as follows:

Take Physical Actions

1. Identify the Stressors or Factors That Cause Your Stress
2. Set Goals for Your Life, Daily, Short-Term, and Long-Term
3. Create an Alternative Plan (Plan B) When Necessary for the Times When Things Do Not Go as Expected
4. Have a Budget for Your Income and Expenses
5. Exercise Your Body
6. Exercise Your Mind
7. Eat the Right Diet
8. Make Time for the Ones You Love and Those That Love You
9. Make Time for Yourself
10. Declutter and Beautify Your Surroundings and Your Mind
11. Protect Your Possessions
12. Know What is the Worst That Could Happen and Take Action to Prevent It
13. Find a Reason to Laugh or Smile Every Day; If You Can't Find One, Create One

Take Mental Actions

1. Accept Yourself as You Are and Make the Change You Want to Become a Better You
2. Learn How to Express Yourself and Communicate
3. Understand and Embrace Your Fears
4. Protect Your Mind and Body from the Environment
5. Find Something to Hope For

6. Accept the Things You Cannot Change, Know the Difference and Change What You Can
7. You Don't Have to Win Every Conflict—Avoid Unnecessary Ones
8. Release the Quest to Be in Control, Because You Will Never Be
9. Avoid Procrastination
10. Allow Yourself to Make Intentional Decisions
11. Never Make Important Decisions Based On Your Emotions. Do Not Allow Yourself to Take Actions Simply Because You Have the Power to Do So, Particularly When They Affect Others Adversely.
12. Yes, it is OK to Say No
13. Do Not Allow Yourself to Be Pulled from Your Daily Plan to Fit in Someone Else's Unless it is Extremely Important and Mutually Beneficial to Both Parties
14. Be Focused and Committed to Your Ultimate Goals and Aspirations; Do Not Allow Yourself to Be Distracted by Others in Your Personal, Social, Business, or Professional Life.
15. Lose Your Toxic Relationships
16. Avoid Destructive Behaviors
17. Let Go of Negative Emotions
18. Focus on Your Own Goals and Visions; Do Not Burden Yourself Thinking About Other People's Money, Status, or Success; Neither Be Envious of Them

19. Do Not Get into Any Agreement, Contract, Business, Investment, or Anything in Which You Have Limited or No Knowledge and Understanding
20. Create and Develop a Mind That Is Not Controlled by Ideology, Politics, or Religion
21. Find a quiet place of solitude and allow your mind to harness the energy you need to function in a world that is changing every moment
22. Be Gracious, Give Thanks for Everything

Take Community Actions

1. Take Time Out of Your Life to Help Others
2. The very thought of giving to others can fill your heart with joy even before you commit the act of giving
3. Find Someone to Love
4. Resolve or Decrease Conflicts within Family
5. Know the Importance of Friends and Relationships
6. Find Yourself a Mentor and Be a Mentor for Others
7. Find Something to Do
8. Know the Wishes of Your Loved Ones Before They Are Silent
9. Communicate About Your Sexual Relationships
10. Reduce the Risks of Healthcare Crisis—Illness
11. Protect Your Possessions
12. Whenever You Employ Someone, Make Sure That You Understand the Scope of Work You are Expecting from Them and What is Involved—Do Your Research

13. Share Your Goals and Aspirations with Those Who Truly Mean You Well
14. Find Your Spiritual or Your Universal Center
15. Get Professional Help

I have used the acronym S.T.R.E.S.S. to provide a simple way to guide you when you are stressed: identify your **S**tressors—factors that cause you to be stressed; determine the **T**ime required for the stress to be under control; identify the **R**easons why these factors cause you to be stressed; identify the order of **E**mergency for each factor; identify **S**olutions for these factors, and identify who or what **S**upport you can get to help you resolve the issues related to these factors that cause you to be stressed.

In this world, life can be really difficult and challenging for some people, more so than others. One thing that always makes a difference is each person taking personal responsibility for their own actions. Also helpful is working diligently to find solutions for the challenges they face and knowing that they still have some control that can significantly influence the outcome of any circumstances regardless of how difficult things may be. This is primarily because our mind, whatever we allow to be its driving force, will often determine where we are at any given point in our lives, both physically and mentally. Let us protect our mind and allow it to guide us to a better place where our stress will be what we allow it to be.

In writing this book, it is my hope that the information contained will, in part, be the stimulus that causes you to take actions that will ultimately lead to a reduction of your stress level. I know that I have given you a lot to put into action and make that a part of your reality. Therefore, much is required of you. But I also want to leave with you a personal confession: in as much as I am asking these things of you, I am also requiring the same of me. The success I have attained in life and continue to achieve is in part because of some of these principles. Therefore, I will continue to strive to take the actions indicated in this book. So, I ask you to join me on this journey as we all strive to find better ways to deal with stress and enjoy a better life.

I truly hope that after you have completed this book, you will find satisfaction and sureness in knowing that you can transform or transition your life to a state of greater tranquility and relaxation with relief or reprieve from some of life's challenges. I also hope that you will feel a sense of ease and equanimity that allows you to find serenity and take solace in knowing that your mind is at a better place as you embrace the reality of tremendous success while you soar to the summit of your dreams....To that end, I say:

> The capacity that we have to do anything, whether we believe in our ability or that of others, is often determined by how committed we are in challenging our own beliefs. — D. Terrence Foster.[7,15]

Finally, to everyone who is a part of this journey with me, I want you to know that................*I am eternally grateful!*

Suggested Readings, References, and Resources

1. The American Psychiatric Association (APA) https://www.psychiatry.org/
2. American Society of Addiction Medicine https://www.asam.org/
3. "A Syndrome Produced by Diverse Nocuous Agents" – 1936 article by Hans Selye from The Journal of Neuropsychiatry and Clinical Neurosciences
4. Selye, H. *The Stress of Life* (New York: McGraw-Hill, 1956), ISBN 978-0070562127
5. Selye, H. (Oct 7, 1955). *"Stress and disease." Science. 122 (3171): 625–631. Bibcode:1955Sci...122..625S. doi:10.1126/science.122.3171.625. P MID 13255902.*
6. Siang Yong Tan, MD1 and A Yip, MS2. Hans Selye (1907–1982): Founder of the stress theory. https://www.ncbi.nlm.nih.gov/pmc/articles/PMC59 15631/
7. Foster, D Terrence, MD. *The Opioid Epidemic: Consumers and Healthcare Guide* (Morrow, Ga.: Global Health and Consortium Publishing, 2019).
8. Osteen, Joel. *Your Best Life Now: 7 Steps to Living at Your Full Potential* (New York: Warner Faith Hachette Book Group, 2004).
9. The Association of the Global Organization for Stress. http://www.gostress.com/stress-facts/
10. The American Institute of Stress https://www.stress.org/daily-life

11. American Psychological Association, Stress in America™ 2020 A National Mental Health Crisis https://www.apa.org/news/press/releases/stress/2020/report-october

12. Gibran, Khalil. *The Prophet* (New York: Knopf, 1923).

13. Substance Abuse and Mental Health Services Administration https://www.samhsa.gov/multi-site-search?search_api_fulltext=STRESS

14. *Physical Activity Guidelines for Americans, 2nd edition* (2018). https://health.gov/sites/default/files/2019-09/Physical_Activity_Guidelines_2nd_edition.pdf

15. Goodreads; https://www.goodreads.com/?ref=nav_home

16. Hill, Napoleon. *Think and Grow Rich* (New York: Ballantine Books,1990).

17. Obama, Barack. *The Audacity of Hope* (New York: Crown Publishing Group, 2006).

18. Covey, Stephen R. *The Seven Habits of Highly Effective People* (New York: Simon & Schuster, 1990).

19. Stux, Gabriel and Bruce Pomeranz. *Basics of Acupuncture Fourth Edition* (New York: Springer, 1997).

20. https://addicted2success.com/

21. https://www.goalcast.com/

22. *Hackett, Conrad; Mcclendon, David (2015). "Christians remain world's largest religious group, but they are declining in Europe". Pew Research Center.*

23. National Suicide Prevention Lifeline at 1-800-273-TALK (8255), available 24 hours a day, 7 days a week. Lifeline chat is a service available to everyone.

24. Brito, Janet, Ph.D., LCSW, CST —Abrams Mere LCSW. 46 Terms That Describe Sexual Attraction, Behavior, and Orientation on. December 10, 2019 https://www.healthline.com/health/different-types-of-sexuality

25. Brito, Janet, Ph.D., LCSW, CST —Abrams Mere, LCS. 64 Terms That Describe Gender Identity and Expression. December 20, 2019 https://www.healthline.com/health/different-genders

26. Nolte, John Ph.D. *The Human Brain: An Introduction to Its Functional Anatomy* (Philadelphia: The C. V. Mosby Company, 1988).

27. Kiyosaki, Robert. *Rich Dad Poor Dad: What the Rich Teach Their Kids About Money* (New York: First Warner Books Printing, 2000).

28. Gray, John Ph.D. *Men Are from Mars. Women Are from Venus: The Classic Guide to Understanding the Opposite Sex* (New York: Harper Paperbacks, 2012).

29. The Changing Global Religious Landscape. Pew Research Center April 5, 2017. The Changing Global Religious Landscape | Pew Research Center (pewforum.org)

30. https://wisdomtoinspire.com/t/dalai-lama/4yru9Zmt/whether-one-believes-in-a-religion-or-not-and-whether-one-believes-in-rebirth-or-not

31. https://www.nytimes.com/2000/02/29/us/2000-campaign-arizona-senator-mccain-denounces-political-tactics-christian-right.html

32. https://www.seattletimes.com/opinion/letters-to-the-editor/heed-the-wise-words-of-john-mccain/
33. https://founders.archives.gov/documents/Jefferson/01-31-02-0445
34. Quotefancy: Wallpapers With Inspirational Quotes
35. A-Z Quotes | Quotes for All Occasions (azquotes.com)
36. https://bookroo.com/quotes/partner
37. https://quotepark.com/quotes/883735-td-jakes-silence-isnt-golden-and-it-surely-doesnt-mean-co/
38. https://www.quotetab.com/quote/by-t-d-jakes/silence-isnt-golden-and-it-surely-doesnt-mean-consent-so-start-practicing-the
39. Pinterest
40. https://sermons.love/joel-osteen/3414-joel-osteen-ask-big.html
41. https://www.passiton.com/inspirational-quotes/6933-everybody-can-be-great-because-anybody-can
42. https://www.oxfordreference.com/view/10.1093/acref/9780191843730.001.0001/q-oro-ed5-00007046
43. https://quoteinvestigator.com/2017/10/23/be-change/
44. Medium – Where good ideas find you.
45. https://www.inspiringquotes.us/author/7893-anwar-sadat
46. https://www.washingtoninstitute.org/media/3591
47. https://libquotes.com/barack-obama/quote/lbu4k1o
48. Inspirational Quotes at BrainyQuote
49. https://www.positivitysparkles.com/quote/dont-like-something-change-cant-change-change-attitude-maya-angelou/

50. https://www.quotespedia.org/authors/l/les-brown/too-many-of-us-are-not-living-our-dreams-because-we-are-living-our-fears-les-brown/
51. https://www.quotespedia.org/authors/a/albert-einstein/if-you-want-to-live-a-happy-life-tie-it-to-a-goal-not-to-people-or-things-albert-einstein/
52. https://364life.com/2017/12/20/endless-echoes/
53. https://quotedb.org/marcus-garvey-quotes/
54. https://www.fearlessmotivation.com/2018/08/06/you-never-know-how-strong-you-are-until-being-strong-is-the-only-choice-you-have/
55. https://www.reddit.com/r/AskLiteraryStudies/comments/j1ox7d/source_of_james_baldwin_quote_i_cant_believe_what/
56. https://www.randomactsofkindness.org/kindness-quotes/184-carry-out-a-random-act
57. https://www.posterenvy.com/princess-diana-carry-out-a-random-act-of-kindness-with-no-expectation-of-reward-safe-in-the-knowledge-that-one-day-someone-might-do-the-same-for-you/
58. https://www.overallmotivation.com/quotes/margaret-thatcher-quotes/
59. https://www.quora.com/Abraham-Lincoln-said-Nearly-all-men-can-stand-the-test-of-adversity-but-if-you-really-want-to-test-a-mans-character-give-him-power-Why-are-people-so-vulnerable-to-power
60. https://www.fluentu.com/blog/spanish/quotes-in-spanish/
61. https://graciousquotes.com/bill-gates/

62. https://blog.acton.org/archives/91697-6-quotes-ronald-reagan-freedom.html

63. http://www.digitalhistory.uh.edu/disp_textbook.cfm?smtid=3&psid=1234

64. https://underground.net/the-world-will-not-be-destroyed-by-those-who-do-evil-but-by-those-who-watch-them-without-doing-anything-%E2%80%95-albert-einstein/

65. https://millyuns.com/quotes-robert/

66. https://elitesavvy.com/2017/02/24/20-inspirations-robert-f-smith-the-secrets-to-wealth-creation/

67. https://robertfsmith.org/transcript

68. https://robertfsmith.org/

69. https://www.fearlessmotivation.com/2021/05/04/things-napoleon-hill-said/

70. https://www.inc.com/jeff-haden/43-best-napoleon-hill-quotes-to-inspire-success-in-life-business.html

71. https://quoteinvestigator.com/2013/01/10/watch-your-thoughts/

72. https://wisdomtoinspire.com/t/confucius/4JWR565lg/never-impose-on-others-what-you-would-not-choose-for-yourself

73. https://en.wikipedia.org/wiki/Golden_Rule

74. https://www.azquotes.com/quote/377079

75. https://themormonworkerdotnet.wordpress.com/past-issues/mw-issue-6/killing-for-ideology-a-brief-history-of-us-efforts-to-establish-a-free-market-capitalist-economy-in-iraq/

76. https://succeedfeed.com/colin-powell-quotes/

77. https://graciousquotes.com/colin-powell/
78. https://www.reddit.com/r/GetMotivated/comments/bfs2w8/text_we_spend_so_much_time_being_afraid_of/
79. https://www.forbes.com/quotes/11194/
80. https://www.reddit.com/r/rockets/comments/j39qs4/ive_missed_more_than_9000_shots_in_my_career_ive/
81. https://www.quotespedia.org/authors/d/dolly-parton/dont-get-so-busy-making-a-living-that-you-forget-to-make-a-life-dolly-parton/
82. https://medium.com/publishous/the-meaning-behind-the-desiderata-poem-8c2e3296d6cb
83. https://www.desiderata.com/desiderata.html
84. Https://www.yahoo.com/lifestyle/9-healthy-eating-quotes-motivate-150000510.html
85. https://quotedb.org/marcus-garvey-quotes/
86. https://www.theplanningcenter.com/happy-life
87. https://succeedfeed.com/zig-ziglar-quotes/
88. https://www.quoteish.org/2018/03/gratitude-quotes.html
89. https://www.beaninspirer.com/significance-friendship-matters/
90. https://quotefancy.com/quote/1134140/Madonna-Family-is-everything-Family-comes-first-It-s-not-what-I-expected-it-to-be-but
91. https://quotefancy.com/quote/879847/Oprah-Winfrey-The-way-through-the-challenge-is-to-get-still-and-ask-yourself-What-is-the
92. https://www.brainyquote.com/quotes/maya_angelou_383371
93. https://www.quotetab.com/quote/by-oprah-winfrey/you-teach-people-how-to-treat-you?source=people

94. https://www.brainyquote.com/quotes/ronald_reagan_147717

95. https://www.washingtonpost.com/opinions/trust-but-verify-an-untrustworthy-political-phrase/2016/03/11/da32fb08-db3b-11e5-891a-4ed04f4213e8_story.html

96. https://www.pinterest.com/pin/382806655556237286/

97. https://clark.com/

98. https://blog.shrimpy.io/blog/7-proven-ways-to-safeguard-your-cryptocurrencies

99. https://uniswap.org/

100. https://www.coinbase.com/learn/crypto-basics

101. https://www.forbes.com/quotes/author/calvin-coolidge/

102. https://www.pinterest.com/pin/259519997257359300/

103. https://www.brainpickings.org/2018/07/13/kahlil-gibran-prophet-love/

104. https://www.annualcreditreport.com/index.action

105. https://www.lyricfind.com/

106. https://www.pewresearch.org/wp-content/uploads/2018/07/FT_18.06.28_MedicalTreatment_most-americans-high-costs.png?w=420

107. https://www.cms.gov/Research-Statistics-Data-and-Systems/Statistics-Trends-and-Re-ports/NationalHealthExpendData/NationalHealthAccountsHistorical

108. https://www.cms.gov/files/document/nations-health-dollar-where-it-came-where-it-went.pdf

109. https://www.brainyquote.com/authors/chris-tucker-quotes

110. https://wealthygorilla.com/chris-tucker-quotes/

111. https://health.gov/sites/default/files/2019-09/Physical_Activity_Guidelines_2nd_edition.pdf

112. https://www.espn.com/olympics/story/_/id/31912437/sponsors-laud-simone-biles-prioritizing-mental-health

113. https://www.forbes.com/sites/pauladavis/2021/07/28/simone-biles-mental-health--the-pressure-to-be-perfect/?sh=652fb2ce5a1e

114. www.abstractkidnapping.com

INDEX

ABOUT THE AUTHOR

D. Terrence Foster, M.D., MA, FAAPMR, DABPM

Dr. Foster graduated from the Albert Einstein College of Medicine of Yeshiva University, New York, earning his Doctor of Medicine. At the City University of New York, he received a master's degree in Chemistry from the University of the West Indies, a Bachelor of Science, BS (Hons), in Chemistry. His medical training was completed at Jacobi Medical Center/Albert Einstein Hospital, New York (Internship). His Residency was at New York University Medical Center/Rusk Institute of Rehabilitation Medicine-Physical Medicine & Rehabilitation, and the Medical College of Wisconsin, Milwaukee (Fellowship), Electrodiagnostic Medicine (EMG).

Dr. Foster worked as an attending physician and clinical instructor at Emory University Hospitals, Wesley Woods Geriatric Hospital, and the Center for Rehab Medicine. In addition, he is a former medical director for The Rehabilitation Center at Southern Regional Health System in Riverdale, Georgia, where he served for ten years.

Dr. Foster has medical staff privileges at several medical centers in the state of Georgia. He is currently the medical director for the Center for Pain and Rehab Medicine in Stockbridge, Georgia, where his primary focus is Interventional Pain and Addiction Medicine.

He is Board Certified in Physical Medicine and Rehabilitation and a fellow of the American Academy of Physical Medicine and Rehabilitation. He is also a Diplomate of the American Board of Physical Medicine and Rehabilitation. He is Board Certified in Pain Medicine and a Diplomate of the American Board of Pain Medicine.

Dr. Foster is the author or co-author of several scientific articles. He is the author of the books **Foster's Opioid Addiction Classification Status Guide** & **The Opioid Epidemic: Consumers and Healthcare Guide.**

Dr. Foster is a strong supporter of many charitable organizations. He is also the Chairman and CEO of the D. Terrence Foster Foundation Inc. He also serves on several non-profit organizations' boards of directors in the Atlanta area.

He also previously hosted a radio show called "The Doctor Show." In addition, he is a member of several medical associations.

Visit his website at DTerrenceFoster.com

Photo by: Atlanta Photographers Network.

OTHER MEDIA PLATFORMS AND INFORMATION ABOUT THE AUTHOR

Check out my latest books on Amazon https://tinyurl.com/ydcbnozr

Visit my website https://www.dterrencefoster.com/

D. Terrence Foster Foundation Inc: https://www.dtffinc.com/

Twitter: https://twitter.com/DRDTFOSTER

Instagram: https://www.instagram.com/drdtfoster

Facebook: https://www.facebook.com/DRDTFOSTER

LinkedIn: https://www.linkedin.com/in/d-terrenc

YouTube Channel https://www.youtube.com/channel/UCm8KEgUyxR-FrAEy6obthYA/about

OTHER BOOKS BY DR. FOSTER

FOCAS

OTHER BOOKS - DR. FOSTER

THE OPIOID EPIDEMIC

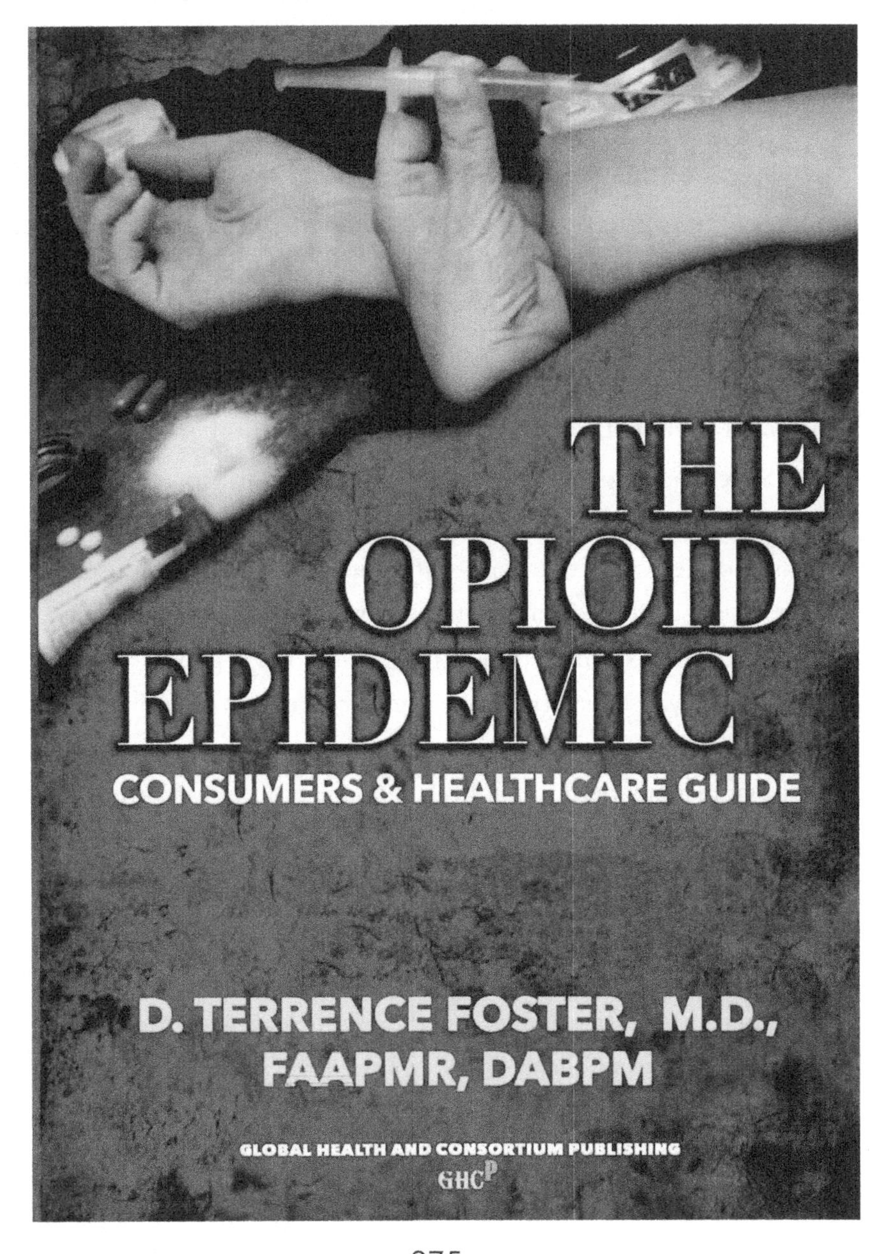

ACKNOWLEDGMENTS

The writing of this book is a total collaboration of many different forces coming together. I have benefited from the expertise, knowledge, kindness, as well as so many people's professionalism that has made this book better than I could have made it myself.

I want to take the opportunity to thank my beloved wife, Maxine, for her contribution to the completion of this project.

Special thanks also to everyone who participated in our free/uncompensated, honest, independent, and impartial pre-publication review of this book at the initial draft of the manuscript. Your insight and recommendations have proven invaluable in the development and completion of this book. I am genuinely grateful for the time you have contributed and your excellent constructive comments and reviews that you have provided. You have made this book significantly better than I could imagine. Any criticism of this book rests solely on my shoulders and no one else.

I'm also grateful to those who endorsed this book after the manuscript. Your time and your kindness mean a lot to me, and I appreciate you for participating in this book's development before its publication. The names of the endorsers and those who participated in prepublication reviews are listed in the endorsement sections of the book and online.

Special thanks to the Bradley Communications Corp of professionals dedicated to enhancing the quality of work that authors produced and their personal development. I am grateful for the professional counseling provided by Steve Harrison, Geoffrey Berwind, Cristina Smith, Danette Kubanda, Tamra Richardt, and others. In so many ways, you have taken me to a higher level as an author and communicator than I have ever been before. For that, I am truly grateful.

Special thanks to the editor Rachel L. Shuster, copy editor and proofreader Abigail Gibbs and index by Paul Sutliff. The book cover design by Usama Zaheen. You have all contributed to a book that we all can be proud of.

Finally, to the many people who made their contribution choosing the cover of this book from several other options, I just want to say special thanks to you for being a part of this process.

BRIEF SUMMARY OF
THE STRESS BOOK

FORTY-PLUS WAYS TO MANAGE STRESS & ENJOY YOUR LIFE

This book takes a comprehensive approach to stress management and how modifying your lifestyle and taking practical steps can significantly reduce the level of stress you are experiencing. More than **forty** approaches to stress reduction management and prevention are covered in this book, giving you an in-depth framework applicable to most lives and circumstances.

This book also provides you with many opportunities to simplify the management of stress by using the acronym **S.T.R.E.S.S.** and incorporating any of the forty-plus actions included. In addition, you are provided with practical ideas, solutions, or options that, when applied, are likely to result in the reduction or prevention of your stress. This book is intended to significantly improve people's lives at any level of society who may be experiencing stress in their personal, business, or professional lives. I trust that it will make a difference in yours.

Thank you for taking the journey to improve stress in your life and for reading this book.

Dr. D. Terrence Foster

PRAISE FOR THE STRESS BOOK

The world we live in is full of stress in one form or another - physical, emotional, and financial, etc.

This book is a delightful guide full of important information for everybody who wants to learn how to deal with stress. It's like food for the soul. It offers practical step-by-step exercises to bring the seed of peace by learning management skills. This outstanding book reflects Dr. Foster's deep wisdom and his desire to help people on the path to a stress-free life.

I strongly recommend this book and believe if everybody reads it, the world will be a more peaceful place full of joy and happiness. Dr. Foster has used acronyms, straightforward terminology, or words in this book to make it easy and simple for the general public.

Congratulations to Dr. Foster for making an effort to reach everybody through his book for stress-free living.

Arun Munjal, Board Certified Psychiatrist.

Having spent my career in the field of stress and trauma diagnosis and healing, I fully recognize the completeness of Dr. Foster's informative and comprehensive volume of stress management action plans. Take his wise advice and "become the CEO of your life." Stress is a normal response to abnormal conditions and is a bio-psycho-social function present in all living organisms. It is clear that Dr. Foster understands how too much of a good thing for too long may become a disorder, as in Post Traumatic Stress Disorder. I envision the reader highlighting areas of need and marking passages that could serve to create talking and treatment points to inform any therapeutic advisor.

The Stress Book is replete with handy charts, graphs, and chapter summaries, as well as meaningful quotes ranging from Lao Tzu to Dolly Parton. Because Dr. Foster knows one size does not fit all, he puts you in the driver's seat as you choose from the myriad Stress Solution Support lists for use in your own life. I won't be surprised when this book becomes your best bedside friend.

It was an honor and pleasure to review and endorse your manuscript.

Professor Emerita Ann K. Neuropsychologist & Author of Four Books.

Dr. Foster's body of literary work is a "How-to" manual that teaches not only how to identify stressors in its many disguises but offers roadmap solutions on how to rid ourselves of them and rebuild our lives with positive energy.

The Action Steps on the Physical, Mental, and Community levels provide a network of support that serves as the indispensable Hub supplying the right mix of grace, strength, and drive needed at each level of one's transformation journey.

Dr. Foster's book reaches deep into the dark recesses of our minds, shines the light on the things we've tried so hard to normalize, then points us to a better way of living – stress-free living!

Rev. Dr. Cleveland L. Thomas, ThD. Senior Pastor. Trinity Pentecostal Church of God.

A Class Above the Rest Because Pain Now Has a Solution

The Stress Book: Forty-plus Ways to Manage Stress is a must-read for anyone who is undergoing stress on a daily basis or believes they are in a state of imbalance and hopelessness due to stress-related issues of life.

In over 35 years of practicing as a Mental Health Therapist, rarely have I had the pleasure of reading a book which addresses stress in such a compelling, thought-provoking manner as has been masterfully presented by Dr. D. Terrence Foster; one which appeals to the total person—mind, body, and soul.

Dr. Foster draws upon his expansive medical experience and offers his readers practical solutions to overcoming stress which, when put into intentional practice, should yield transformative results. Improvement begins with a single step in a positive direction, and that step would be in partaking of the valuable nuggets imparted within these pages.

Maxwell Sears, MA/LPC/Therapist/cPhD. Caya Counseling Services, Inc.

It has been my pleasure and privilege to read the manuscript of Dr. Foster's well written, comprehensive, informative, and easy to read book. Whether you read it cover to cover, or focus on selected chapters and topics, you will benefit from the many practical suggestions for reducing stress levels.

Clover Hall, Ed.D., (Retired) Vice President of Institutional Research and Academic Planning, Community Advocate

----

As a communication and visual media specialist who's worked through high stress situations in Corporate America and on University campuses, I have seen many life-altering examples of how important it is to engage with therapeutic resources to understand how to release ourselves from things that hold us back from our true potential, from our ability to thrive, and from each of us living our best life. Stress is a barrier that can be alleviated when you find a path toward understanding and communicating what's holding you back. Start with Dr. Foster's The Stress Book. It is a great resource.

Dr. Joan V. Golding: Communication and Visual Media Specialist.

Dr. Foster's book is an ideal book at present times for stress management in our daily life. Must read; it is practical, inspiring, and can lead to life-changing, positive influences.

Brij Gulati, MD, Psychiatrist.

Made in United States
North Haven, CT
10 August 2024